Minding the Body, Mending the Mind

UPDATED AND REVISED

Joan Borysenko, PhD

WITH LARRY ROTHSTEIN

MJF BOOKS
NEW YORK

Published by MJF Books
Fine Communications
322 Eighth Avenue
New York, NY 10001

Minding the Body, Mending the Mind
LC Control Number: 2014945383
ISBN 978-1-60671-266-5

Illustrations by Neal Rohrer, Neal Rohrer Designs

This edition is published by MJF Books in arrangement with Da Capo Press,
a member of the Perseus Books Group.

Printed in the United States of America.

QF   10   9   8   7   6   5   4   3   2   1

To Miroslav Borysenko
Once husband, always friend

CONTENTS

Foreword   ix

Acknowledgments   xi

   Introduction to the New Edition   1

1 The Science of Healing   11

2 Getting Back in Control   35

3 Breaking the Anxiety Cycle   63

4 Mindfulness and the Discovery of the Self   99

5 Mind Traps: Outwitting the Dirty Tricks
   Department of the Mind   123

6 Reframing and Creative Imagination   151

7 Healing the Emotions   171

8 Sam's Story: Amazing Grace   203

   Epilogue: Putting It All Together:
   Twelve Brief Reminders   223

Additional Reading   231

Self-Assessment   235

Index   248

FOREWORD

When I first met Dr. Borysenko in the late 1970s, she was a young cancer researcher on the faculty of the Tufts University School of Medicine in Boston, teaching both histology (microscopic anatomy) and an unusual elective course in what was then called holistic medicine. On her lunch breaks she taught hatha yoga and meditation, sometimes inviting students and colleagues back to her laboratory to sample healthful vegetarian fare afterward. Those impromptu samplings often included organic produce from her garden and wild foods foraged from the fields and forests surrounding the rural Massachusetts home where she lived. Among those foods were mushrooms she'd collected as a passionate amateur mycologist.

Joan's personal interest in health and natural living, coupled with her academic expertise in medical science, placed her at the leading edge of the field that later evolved into integrative medicine, which is my passion. In the twenty years that have passed since she wrote *Minding the Body, Mending the Mind* it has taken its place as an enduring classic. The book found its way into college and medical school classrooms, doctors' offices, and hundreds of thousands of households. Joan outlines a simple, yet comprehensive and effective, approach to mental and physical well-being that has stood the test of time and the trials of modern research.

Diet and exercise are now universally recognized as critical factors affecting health and well-being. Healing practices originating in the East—from hatha yoga to acupuncture and chi gong—are now used as adjuncts to Western medicine. We have much evidence that meditation reduces stress and enhances immunity; now sophisticated neuroimaging studies show that it also stimulates areas of the brain that regulate happiness. And although pharmaceutical drugs have their place in the treatment of severe conditions, natural remedies, stress reduction, and lifestyle change can often achieve results that are equal to or better than prescription medications with far less risk and expense in the management of common ailments.

Whether you're a young person who hopes to live a healthy, vital, and happy life; an older person who is trying to age well and maintain your energy level and physical function; a stressed-out person yearning for balance; or someone with an acute or chronic illness that you'd like to address on all levels—body, mind, and spirit—this book can help you. It's practical, easy to understand, and based on solid research that you can trust. Furthermore, *Minding the Body, Mending the Mind* is an inspiring exploration of what it means to be fully human—present in each moment with an open mind and an open heart. In the last analysis, that may be one of the best definitions of well-being and what it means to live your best life.

Andrew Weil, M.D.
Tucson, Arizona
May 2007

ACKNOWLEDGMENTS

Much of the wisdom in this book is a gift from more than two thousand patients who participated in the Mind/Body Clinic that I directed at the Beth Israel Hospital in Boston, Massachusetts (now part of the Beth Israel/Deaconess Medical Center), from 1981 to 1987. I thank each and every one of them, for they were—and continue to be—my teachers.*

The process of writing (and revising) this book stimulated recollections of my ongoing evolution from worrier to warrior—a quip that I attribute to my colleague Ilan Kutz, M.D., who helped found the Mind/Body Clinic with Herbert Benson, M.D., and me in September 1981. Without their outstanding vision and expertise neither the clinical programs nor this book would have existed.

I first worked with Dr. Benson as a graduate student in the Department of Pharmacology at the Harvard Medical School in the late 1960s, and again from 1978 to 1988, when he was the

---

*Please note that all references to patients or other individuals used as examples are pseudonyms and are often composites of more than one person's experience. All identifying characteristics have been changed to honor confidentiality.

chief of the Division of Behavioral Medicine, first at Boston's Beth Israel Hospital, and then at the New England Deaconess Hospital. It was my good fortune to be one of the first postdoctoral fellows on the National Institutes of Health grant that he was awarded in 1978 to train health professionals in the newly emerging field of behavioral medicine. From there, under his tutelage, I became an instructor in medicine at the Harvard Medical School and was given the opportunity to cofound the Mind/Body Clinic and to participate in the division's research efforts. I remain most grateful for these remarkable opportunities, which helped to shape my life.

I owe a very special thanks to Jon Kabat-Zinn, Ph.D., whose Stress Reduction and Relaxation Program at the University of Massachusetts Medical School was an early model for the Mind/Body Clinical Programs. His help was invaluable to us. Dr. Kabat-Zinn's deep understanding of mindfulness enriched me personally as well as informed both the clinical programs and this book. His leadership in mindfulness-based stress reduction has revolutionized the field of behavioral medicine in the ensuing decades, and his friendship has been a blessing.

Stephen Maurer, M.A., dropped by the Beth Israel Hospital for lunch in October 1983 and stayed on as a source of nourishment for us all, becoming the assistant director of the Mind/Body Clinic during my tenure, and then its director for a period in the late 1980s after I'd moved on. His understanding of meditation and the mind added substantial depth both to the programs and to this book, as did his wit and warmth. The chapter on mind traps is adapted from a system that Steve first introduced to us, and many of the stories about meditation are also Steve's gifts.

Without his bright mind and good heart, both the clinic and this book would have been far less successful than they have been.

Jane Leserman, Ph.D., a dear friend and colleague through the years, did wonderful work in the 1980s evaluating the clinical programs and developing self-assessment tools, including the medical and psychological symptoms checklists at the back of the book. Her guidance and collaboration are very much appreciated, and they helped make the research on our clinical programs possible. Steven Locke, M.D., shared his interest and enthusiasm in psychiatry and psychoneuroimmunology frequently "back in the day." I thank him for his friendship, for his support, and for many stimulating conversations.

Although I am responsible for writing this book—and for the personal viewpoints expressed—the ideas on which it is based are neither new nor entirely my own. They represent the synthesis of a collective wisdom that is as old as humanity itself. Many friends and colleagues shared their work and ideas with me through the years, and their wisdom has found its way also onto these pages. Sincere thanks to Olivia Hoblitzelle, M.A.; Eileen Stuart, R.N., M.S.; Margaret Caudill, M.D., Ph.D.; Rachel Naomi Remen, M.D.; Michael Lerner, Ph.D.; Dean Ornish, M.D.; Leo Stolbach, M.D.; Matthew Budd, M.D.; David Eisenberg, M.D.; Robin Casarjian, M.A.; Bernie Siegel, M.D.; and Kenneth Pelletier, Ph.D.

Special thanks to my agent, Helen Rees, who was a champion of this book at a time when mind/body medicine was in its infancy. And without Bill Patrick—my amazing editor at Addison Wesley—this would have been a very different animal altogether. His "roll up the sleeves and teach Joan how to write" enthusiam, together with the collaboration of two talented writers—Larry Rothstein and Ken Rivard—made this book much clearer and more accessible than it might have been if I, as a new writer, had been left to my own devices.

It seems delightful, and just a wee bit odd, to thank my family now for who they were when this book was written. We have all grown and changed in twenty years, of course, but their essence is still embedded in these pages. My former husband, Miroslav Borysenko, was a cherished colleague—a scientist in his own right and a partner in research—during the time that I directed the Mind/Body Clinic and wrote this book. Although we are now divorced, we remain good friends. Our children, who were teens when they graciously allowed me to tell some of their stories in these pages, are now married and the parents of Alex, Eddie, and Sophia—our grandchildren. Life goes on, and my hope is that it will go on a little bit more smoothly for you because of the gifts I've received from so many others—only a few of whom I've had the privilege to mention here. You can honor their gifts by passing them on to your own family and friends. That is how—together— we heal not only ourselves, but our world.

Introduction to the New Edition

Twenty years have passed since I first wrote *Minding the Body, Mending the Mind*. The day I was told that it was going to appear on the *New York Times* best seller list, I was sitting at the desk in my hospital office, reviewing medical charts. The phone rang, and it was George Gibson, the book's publicist, enthusiasm and excitement bubbling through his voice. "Are you sitting down?" he asked breathlessly, before sharing the news. "The *New York Times* best seller list," I mused, unimpressed. "Is that a good thing?"

In the insular world of medical science and clinical practice, best sellers weren't much of a consideration back then. Publication of studies in peer-reviewed journals, where the results of meticulous research were shared with colleagues—now that was something to get excited about. But in the twenty years that have passed, more and more books have appeared aimed at educating (or sometimes taking advantage of) a public that is increasingly stressed out, anxious, alienated, sick, and depressed.

It's a marvel that in the last twenty years we've learned so much about health and well-being. The average person knows more about exercise, diet, psychology, supplements, and pharmaceuticals now than ever before in history. Why, then, is there such an obvious slip between the cup and the lip? *We're more obese, sedentary, and stressed out now than ever before.* And these lifestyle choices impact our health in a serious way. More than 70 percent of all cancers, greater than 80 percent of all heart disease, and over 90 percent of type 2 diabetes are related to unhealthy lifestyles.

Finger pointing doesn't help figure out why we Americans take such poor care of ourselves. Yes, there is a raging fast-food epidemic, spurred by the kind of television commercials that feature lissome young ladies gulping down giant burgers and frolicking in fields of french fries. And surely most of us realize that endless hours of staring at computer monitors or playing video games are no match healthwise for being outside and moving around. And yet, as a society, we've all but forgotten how to inhabit the natural world.

But perhaps *the most obvious explanation for the gap between what we know and how that translates into taking care of our health, is our emotional state.* Dr. Martin Seligman, who founded the field of positive psychology in 1998, cites data that, despite our better standard of living, Americans have become progressively more depressed since World War I—and at a much younger age. Seligman credits self-absorption—being more interested in our own individualistic agenda than in the good of the whole—as one obvious culprit. Altruistic people, who think about helping others, are less depressed and anxious than most— and they live longer. The same is true of those of us who can manage our stress and accentuate the positive rather than marinating in the negative.

When we feel bad—overwhelmed by anxiety, uncertainty, depression, and stress—most of us act in the most human possible way. We try to comfort ourselves. But going to the gym, jumping on a bike, or even taking a walk isn't most people's first choice for comfort. It's easier to numb out watching the television, hunting for happiness in cyberspace, drinking, smoking, doing drugs, or eating something full of fat, sugar, or salt that is instantly satisfying.

I'm convinced—as a medical scientist, a psychologist, a busy professional, a mother, a grandmother, and a wife—that taking care of the mind, which in turn generates our emotions, is the missing link when it comes to taking care of the body. I learned this lesson many years ago. When I was twenty-four I was working on my doctoral dissertation at the Harvard Medical School, investigating the way cells maintain their attachment to one another. I was living on coffee and cigarettes, broke and tired, trying to cope with a troubled marriage and an infant son for whom I had far too little time. Furthermore, I was a relentless perfectionist, trying to control and succeed at everything. My emotions were in an uproar, and anxiety and irritability were my constant companions.

I was also a physical wreck. Troubled by migraines all my life, I found that the intense competition added crippling stomach pains and vomiting to my list of psychosomatic illnesses. As a graduate student, I also came down with severe bronchitis four times in two years and had to study for my doctoral exams while my head spun in a fever. As if this weren't enough, I also developed the high blood pressure that ran in my family.

My marriage fell apart during this year. I was now a single parent plagued with fainting and crippled by abdominal pains that were diagnosed as spastic colon. I was given antispasmodics, painkillers, and tranquilizers—all to no avail. Then a viral infection in the lining of my lungs created suffocating pain that took me to the emergency room of the nearest hospital.

The field of mind/body medicine didn't exist yet, but there was a friend in the lab where I conducted my graduate research who was excited about his new hobby: yoga and meditation. He compared these to a minivacation in which he could switch off his cares and concerns and come out refreshed and ready to tackle whatever came up. My first thought was that meditation was for ascetics who lived in caves. I was a hardheaded scientist, literally killing myself to master the ways of the medical establishment.

Nevertheless, I gave meditation a try—largely out of desperation—practicing each day. The test came a few weeks later while I was sitting at an electron microscope, trying to unlock the secrets of cancer cells. I felt the familiar stabbing behind my right eye, the light sensitivity and nausea that heralded a migraine. It was time for an experiment.

Retreating to my office, I pulled the shades and shut the door. I settled into a chair, relaxed my muscles from head to foot, shifted my breathing from tense chest breathing to relaxed diaphragmatic breathing, and began to meditate. In time the pain subsided. After the meditation was over, I was left with a feeling of having been washed clean, like the earth after a heavy rain. I ran around the laboratory announcing that I had performed the most important experiment of my life. It was the beginning of a tremendous change in my life that led to greater happiness, increased emotional resilience, and a much healthier lifestyle.

In the following chapters, you'll share my journey of healing and those of some of the people I've had the privilege to work with. Many attended the programs that I cofounded with Drs. Herbert Benson and Ilan Kutz at Boston's Beth Israel Hospital, and that I directed between 1981 and 1988. Our programs at the Mind/Body Clinic, which were shown through peer-reviewed research to decrease anxiety, depression, and medical symptoms, and to increase health and well-being, form the basis for many of the recommendations in this book. Although I left the clinic in 1988, Dr. Benson and his colleagues have continued these programs and added to them. They now practice at the Benson-Henry Institute for Mind Body Medicine, located at Boston's Massachusetts General Hospital.

The people I've worked with, both in the early days of the clinic and in the two decades since that time, have ranged in age from seventeen to ninety-three, and they come from all walks of life. Their struggles and victories have been inspirations and challenges that constantly push me beyond the limits of what I know. They are people who want to participate in their own healing but are wary of fads and unproven claims. They are students, executives, housewives, physicians, laborers, scientists, and engineers, and they come with migraine, insomnia, hives, ulcers, allergies, chronic pain, and more serious illnesses such as cancer and AIDS. At times, in this book, the experiences of more than one person are combined in a single story to protect confidentiality and illustrate what I believe to be basic principles.

Many people over the years were referred to me by physicians, often after years of suffering and sometimes after endless rounds of medications that had not worked. As a rule, other therapies had failed because they addressed only the physical symptoms rather than the underlying causes.

Although the problems of a stressed overachiever may appear very different from those of a young mother suffering from multiple sclerosis and different still from those of an older man with cancer, all these people face similar crises. The underlying issues have as much to do with the meaning of life as with learning to use the power of the mind to reduce symptoms.

Major studies indicate that approximately 75 percent of visits to the family practice physician are either for illnesses that will ultimately get better by themselves or for disorders related to anxiety and stress. For these conditions, symptoms can be reduced or cured as the body's own natural healing balance is reinstated. For many other chronic or potentially life-threatening disorders, symptoms may be lessened, but the progress of disease will lead inevitably toward death. Death, after all, is part of the natural progression of life, and its reality can be a powerful reminder to live life in a way that maximizes contentment, creativity, and love. This is what I call healing. And the underlying desire for healing—for wholeness—is what all people have in common, regardless of the condition that needs healing.

In the chapters ahead you'll read about people who seem like yourself and others who seem very different. In the end, what is so miraculous is that, despite our differences, we're all alike. Beyond identities and desires there is a common core of self—an essential humanity whose nature is peace and whose expression in thought, emotion, and action is unconditional love. When we identify with that inner core, respecting and honoring it in others as well as ourselves, we experience healing in every area of life.

Presenting this material in a book, rather than through personal interaction, was a fascinating challenge. Each reader is different, and honoring those differences is the key to learning. With that in mind, be flexible with yourself as you work along with the book. You may want to skim it first for content and then go back and experience the techniques, mastering the tools at your own pace. Alternatively, you might wish to read through quite slowly, taking eight or ten weeks to work along with the program as if you were actually part of a group process. You might even enjoy setting aside two hours once a week to work with the book, practicing the techniques you have learned during the week before moving on to the next chapter.

In writing and updating the first chapter on mind/body interactions, I gave as much scientific background as concisely as I could. You may find that it's too much for you, just right, or perhaps too little. In the first case, you may want to skim the chapter lightly, coming back to it later if you feel the need. In the latter case, you can supplement the material from the reading list provided at the end of the text.

Chapters 2 and 3 are foundational—building the skill of becoming aware of how to mind the body. In these chapters you will learn how to elicit the relaxation response through meditation, breathing, and stretching exercises. The practice of these exercises has two purposes. First, you learn to shift your physiology, gaining control of the stress response and learning to control the autonomic, or automatic, nervous system, as well as learning to let go of tension in the musculoskeletal system. Second, these basic skills begin to train you in the art of observing your mind.

Chapter 4 is a bridge between the fundamental skills of minding the body and the more advanced skills of taming the mind. It concerns a critical area that most of us can immediately relate to: the ability to live life in the moment rather than being wrapped up in memories of the past or worries about the future. The ability to practice mindful awareness, and to be here now, rests on practicing the concentration and breathing exercises that come in the preceding chapters.

Chapters 5 and 6 provide tools for becoming an observer of your mind in a way that allows for a gradual process of waking up to the present by cutting through the conditioning of the past. This work culminates in learning to learn from emotions and to practice present-centered awareness in daily life as introduced in Chapter 7.

The principles presented in the book are brought together in a very personal way in the last chapter, which tells Sam's story, a true-life drama of mind and spirit overcoming the final limitation of the body—death itself. Sam's struggle with AIDS was a powerful healing experience in my own life and in the lives of many who knew him.

Before beginning your healing work with the book, I suggest that you turn to the appendix and complete the self-evaluation of your current physical and emotional state. After finishing the book, when you feel that you understand the ideas and methods, you can reevaluate your well-being by filling out the assessment a second time. Most people find the self-assessment helpful because it makes them more aware of their physical and emotional state. Completing it takes only a few minutes and will add to your self-understanding.

In going through the self-evaluation materials, use them as an opportunity to ask yourself whether you need medical or psychological help in addition to self-help. A book like this is a wonderful adjunct in some cases, or it may be enough by itself, but it's always a good idea to ask for professional help if you have questions.

My own journey of healing began some forty years ago and is still in progress. I hope that my experiences and those of the patients I have learned from and shared with will help you along your way. You may find the precepts of the book challenging, but they are a guidepost for how we become fully alive and compassionate human beings. I wish you all the best on your journey to healing and peace of mind. It's what you were born for.

CHAPTER 1

The Science of Healing

Early in my career, when I was an assistant professor at the Tufts University School of Medicine in Boston, I watched a Chinese film demonstrating acupuncture anesthesia. As assistants twirled a few needles, a surgeon incised a patient's chest, cracked the ribs, and removed a lobe of the lung—all while the patient, his head demurely hidden behind a sheet, talked amiably and sipped tea. I was viewing the film with immunologist Dr. Miroslav Borysenko, and we were both astounded by what we saw. We asked an anesthesiologist who had been seated nearby what he thought about the remarkable demonstration. "It's nothing," our colleague said dismissively. "Just hypnosis." As if that, in itself, would not have been equally remarkable.

Until the last few decades, scientists were often in the position of having to deny what they were seeing, simply because the underlying mechanisms were not understood. Science is a search for explanations, a complex structure built of small, measurable units, yet some things that happen to real people in the real world just don't fit inside the well-established categories.

A subject under hypnosis raises a very real blister on her skin, even though the "hot iron" the hypnotist says he is touching her with is, in reality, an ordinary pencil. In a clinical test, one-third of women receiving placebos instead of chemotherapy still lose their hair. A person with metastatic cancer, who has been told that she has just weeks to live, suddenly rallies and ultimately beats the disease. The latter is a very rare event, but still it happens. How can this be?

Two thousand years ago a woman who had suffered prolonged uterine bleeding approached Jesus of Nazareth. Coming up to him in a crowd, she touched the hem of his garment and was instantly healed. Jesus turned to her and explained that it was her faith that had made her whole. After centuries of slow progress toward rational explanations of the physical world, even scientists can at last begin to appreciate the truth of his assessment. We are entering a new level in the scientific understanding of mechanisms by which faith, belief, and imagination can actually unlock the mysteries of healing.

Today sophisticated neuroimaging techniques, such as positron-emission tomography (PET) scans or functional magnetic resonance imaging (MRI), allow the brain to be scanned while research subjects are studied in a variety of different conditions. In one such study, volunteers received mild electric shocks—with or without the application of an "anesthetic" salve that was actually a placebo. Not only did they feel less pain when they believed that they were anesthetized, but brain areas responsible for the experience of pain were also less active. In a similar type of study, researchers at the University of Wisconsin in Madison found that when study volunteers were exposed to an unpleasant heat stimulus, *their belief that they had control* over how long the heat would last (even though they really didn't) reduced both their perception of pain and activity in the three brain areas most consistently associated with the experience of pain.

In other words, beliefs may start in the mind, but they end in the body. Any woman who has ever given birth understands something about how context alters pain tolerance. In labor I discovered that discomfort was a euphemism, akin to calling Niagara Falls a gentle shower. Yet still, I endured pretty well. Had the pain been due to something frightening, however—say, a burst appendix or a gunshot wound—the same pain would have seemed completely unbearable. Likewise, what stresses one person is an exciting challenge to another. Again, it's the attitude that makes the difference in how they respond to the same event. Through a web of subtle interconnections involving nerve pathways, neurohormones secreted by the brain, and hormones like cortisol and adrenaline secreted by the adrenal glands, attitudes can affect every cell in the body. For better and for worse.

Brain, Mind, and Molecules

My roots are in laboratory research, and for many years I studied the effects of stress—which often involves a perceived lack of control—on health and immunity. The immune system (the body's front line of defense against disease), the cardiovascular system, and the brain and nervous system—all have been explored independently. In recent years, however, neuroscientists working with psychologists and immunologists have forged a new scientific discipline with the tongue-twisting name of psychoneuroimmunology, or PNI, a field that explores the body's most subtle interconnections.

Stress often begins with how you think. And how you think determines how you feel—both emotionally and sometimes physically as well. When your thoughts create strong emotions—whether positive or negative—your brain releases hormones that spread the emotional news to every system of the body. Called neuropeptides, these hormones are informational molecules that telegraph messages to any cell in the body that has receptors for them. Neuroscientist Dr. Candance Pert has been in the forefront of demonstrating that emotions are a powerful link between mind and body through these informational molecules. Neuropeptides make their way into the bloodstream, where they are distributed throughout the body, binding to surface receptors on a multitude of diverse cells. In the twinkling of an eye, then, an emotion that begins in the brain can trigger subtle and complex cellular reponses throughout the body. In turn, neuropeptides manufactured by the immune system, or by different organs, can also affect the brain and emotional state.

What researchers are documenting is a rich and intricate multidirectional communication system linking the brain, the mind, the immune system, and potentially all other systems of the body from the heart, to the lungs, to the skin. This is the pathway through which our emotions and our hopes, fears, and beliefs can affect the body's ability to defend itself and to function optimally in response to the continually changing moment-by-moment demands of life.

The Big Three Negative Emotions: Depression, Anxiety, and Anger

Depression, anxiety, and chronic anger are uncomfortable emotions in themselves—reason enough to want to minimize them. But in addition, we know that they can also have profound effects on physiology and health.* Prospective studies (these are the scientific gold standard because they follow people who are well for years to understand how and why illnesses may eventually develop) show that depression—the most common psychiatric disorder in America—takes a significant toll on health. Depressed people have an increased incidence of coronary heart disease, and for those who already have heart disease, depression can aggravate it, leading to increased disability. Depression makes pain more difficult to cope with, worsens most medical conditions, and can create its own set of physical symptoms—from headache and body aches to neurological and digestive disturbances. Prolonged depression may even be a risk factor for the development of cancer. Depression's cousins, anxiety and hostility, can also increase the risk of coronary heart disease, and anger has been shown to speed up age-related decline in lung function.

Without going into too much detail, there is a particular kind of neuropeptide, called a cytokine, that regulates the body's immune response. Cytokines signal the immune system to gear up

---

*For more information, see the excellent review article by Janice K. Kiecolt-Glaser et al., "Emotions, Morbidity, and Mortality: New Perspectives from Psychoneuroimmunology," *Annual Review of Psychology*, 2002, 53: 83–107. You can locate it on the Internet on Questia.com.

after injury or infection. But if those signals don't turn off in time, inflammation—the increased immune response that initially shows up as heat, swelling, and redness around a cut— damages the body. Chronic inflammation leads to frailty and can lead to a multitude of disabilities associated with aging, such as osteoporosis, type 2 diabetes, arthritis, some cancers, and even Alzheimer's disease.

We know that both depression and anxiety gear up cytokine production, as do physical stress and chronic emotional stress, such as the difficult task of caring for a loved one with Alzheimer's disease. Poor health habits—obesity, smoking, and a sedentary lifestyle—also increase cytokine production. Although easier said than done, it's best, then, to try to free ourselves from the big three—or at least to make them less prevalent in our lives.

The Stress and Relaxation Responses

In the 1940s, Swiss physiologist and Nobel laureate Walter Hesse experimented on the cat brain and discovered that he could produce two diametrically opposed energy states simply by stimulating different areas of the animal's hypothalamus. One state was a kind of "passing gear" for heightened activity; the other was a state of very low energy expenditure characterized by deep rest and relaxation—the bodily equivalent of "neutral."

In the 1970s, Dr. R. Keith Wallace and Dr. Herbert Benson documented a similar state of profound rest in humans who practiced transcendental meditation. Benson's subsequent studies proved that this state could be elicited through any form of mental concentration that distracted individuals from their usual cares and concerns and focused their minds. He termed this innate, hypothalamic mechanism the *relaxation response.*

When the relaxation response is called upon, heart rate and blood pressure drop. Breathing rate and oxygen consumption decline because of the profound decrease in the need for energy. Brain waves shift from an alert beta rhythm to a relaxed alpha or theta rhythm. Blood flow to the muscles decreases, and instead, blood is sent to the brain and skin, producing a feeling of warmth and rested mental alertness. It was by learning to induce the relaxation response that I began to reverse symptoms of stress that were severe enough to send me to the emergency room.

How was it that stress was able to bring on these symptoms in the first place? Scientists believe that the relaxation response evolved as a means of protecting the organism from burnout, and of returning the body to balance after stress. Nature also provided the "passing gear" we call the fight-or-flight response. I'm sure you've felt it many times when you were suddenly afraid, when you were sure someone was breaking into the house, or when the plane you were on suddenly dropped as it hit a pocket of air. Before you knew it, you were breathing fast and shallowly, your palms were sweaty, and your mouth was dry. The fight-or-flight response means your heart is pounding, your blood pressure is up, your muscles are tense, your pupils are dilated, and your skin may even be covered with goose bumps.

This integrated response evolved millions of years ago because it ensured that the whole organism would be ready for action at the slightest hint of danger. The response is still with us today, hardwired into the human body's communication systems, even though in our infinitely more complex world, danger can take the form of unpaid bills or boredom in a marriage or some unspoken dread produced entirely by the imagination. Fighting and fleeing are not very useful options against such dangers. Nevertheless, through the fight-or-flight response, anxiety still has access to the pathway that elevates blood pressure, and stress still activates pathways that lead to muscle tension and thereby to numerous aches, pains, and bodily disorders.

This response is innate—it's built in. You don't have to think about gearing up your autonomic nervous system when your toddler suddenly races out into a busy street. It just happens when the appropriate stimulus—danger—activates the program. The key word here is *appropriate*. Throughout life, we experience some things as frightening that wouldn't induce a fight-or-flight response in another person. But when we become programmed—or conditioned—to respond to the world in an inappropriate way, there doesn't seem to be much choice in the matter. But just as the brain formed new neural pathways that coupled fight-or-flight with the inappropriate stimulus in the first place, we can learn to delete that neural program from our body/mind computer.

Mind/Body Programming

Every time you miss your exit on the highway because you are daydreaming, then "wake up" to discover yourself miles farther down the road, you are demonstrating the power of the unconscious mind. Once something is learned, we don't have to think about it consciously. The task simply repeats itself as soon as we initiate the program—in this case, by putting the key in the ignition. The rest of driving is second nature because our nervous system has been conditioned—or imprinted—with the driving pattern.

Because of our conditioning, we're all creatures of habit. Most people get anxious before taking an exam partly because they have become habituated to feeling anxious at exam time, whether or not the situation at hand is actually threatening. Once we have been threatened by an exam, a neural connection is established. The next time an exam comes up, the probability is that we'll reactivate that same conditioned circuit.

Physiological conditioning is a kind of rapid learning that evolved to help us master cause-and-effect situations that might determine survival. We're all familiar with Pavlov's famous experiment. A dog is given meat powder, which naturally makes him salivate. A bell is then rung every time the meat powder is presented. After a time the dog salivates merely at the sound of the bell. We see the same mechanism operating in ourselves when we're working away contentedly, then glance up at the clock, notice it's lunchtime, and suddenly become hungry.

The mind's power to affect the body through conditioning became crystal clear to me when I was six or seven years old. My Uncle Dick, a confirmed cheese hater, was eating Sunday dinner with us. For dessert there was a cheesecake camouflaged with ripe strawberries. It was so good that he ate two pieces. About an hour later my mother expressed her surprise at Uncle Dick's delight in the dessert, since she knew how much he hated cheese. At the sound of the word *cheese,* Uncle Dick turned pale, began to gag, and ran for the bathroom. It was obvious to me, even as a child, that the problem was not the cheese itself, but some mental conditioning about cheese that produced such a violent reaction.

Many people who receive chemotherapy for cancer get sick to their stomachs from the medication. Soon, through conditioning similar to Uncle Dick's, they begin to get sick before they actually receive the drugs. Some people begin to get nauseous the night before treatment. Others may get nauseous coming to the hospital or even upon seeing their doctor or nurse. They have involuntarily learned to get sick as a conditioned response to the thoughts, sights, and smells of the chemotherapy situation.

What we've learned from Soviet studies following Pavlov's model is that the immune system itself can be conditioned. In this country Dr. Robert Ader and Dr. Nicholas Cohen at the University of Rochester injected rats with an immunosuppressant drug called cyclophosphamide and at the same time added a new taste—saccharin—to the animals' drinking water. The saccharin acted like Pavlov's bell. After a while the rats were suppressing their immunity at the taste of saccharin alone.

Dr. G. Richard Smith and Sandra McDaniel, a physician-and-nurse team at the University of Arkansas for Medical Sciences at the time their research was published, did a pioneering study of the suppression of immune reactions in humans in the 1980s. Once a month for five months, volunteers who had reacted positively in a tuberculin skin test came into the same room with the same arrangement of furniture and the same nurse. Each time they saw a red and a green vial on the desk; each time the contents of the red vial—tuberculin—were injected into the same arm, and the contents of the green vial—a salt solution—were injected into the other.

Month after month the same procedure was followed, and month after month the volunteers had the same reaction to the tuberculin—a red swollen patch on the same arm. There was never any reaction to the injection of the salt solution in the other arm.

On the sixth trial the contents of the vials were switched without the volunteers' knowledge. And this time the volunteers had almost no reaction to the tuberculin. Their expectation that nothing ever happened after the injection from the green vial apparently was enough to inhibit the immune system's powerful inflammatory response to tuberculin.

Conditioning is a powerful bridge between mind and body. The reason is that the body cannot tell the difference between events that are actual threats to survival and events that are present in thought alone. The mind spins out endless fantasies of possible disasters past and future. This tendency to escalate a situation into its worst possible conclusion is what cognitive psychologist Dr. Albert Ellis dubbed "awfulizing," and it can be a key factor in tipping the balance toward illness or health. Perhaps you're hung up in traffic, sure to be late for an important 9 a.m. meeting. Or it's midnight and your child is still out, or the doctor tells you she wants to repeat a test, and so on in endless variation. The flood of "what ifs" and "if onlys" engages the various human emotions, which can influence virtually all bodily functions.

The way our minds work—the degree to which we awfulize—also depends on genetic predisposition and previous conditioning. The responses of our parents and other influential role models shape our own reactions to life. Awareness of our conditioning is the first step toward unlearning attitudes that have outlived their usefulness. Such awareness opens our ability to respond to what is happening *now* rather than reacting out of a conditioned history that may be archaic. This is the skill you will learn if you really apply yourself to the techniques outlined in the following chapters.

The Dangers of Helplessness

The acute stresses of life produce temporary physiological responses from which the body recovers. It's the chronic stresses—often caused by conditioned negative attitudes and feelings of helplessness—that are the real challenge to healing. Feeling constantly helpless can upset your endocrine balance, elevating the immunosuppressant hormone cortisol and destroying its natural diurnal rhythm. Chronic helplessness also depletes the brain of the vital neurotransmitter norepinephrine, one of the chemicals necessary for feelings of happiness and contentment. Immunological studies, too, reveal that the inability to feel in control of stress, rather than the stressful event itself, is the most damaging to immunity.

Most of us eventually will feel that life is out of control in some way. Whether we see this as a temporary situation whose resolution will add to our store of knowledge and experience or as one more threat demonstrating life's dangers is the most crucial question both for the quality of our lives and our physical health.

Our ability to create the conditions of life most dear to us—realizing our hopes and dreams, goals, and aspirations—depends on having control both over events that we initiate ourselves and over those that come into our lives unbidden—the seeming stresses, obstacles, and disappointments. Without the conviction that we have some control—coupled with the realization that we can't control everything—we have no way to negotiate the tides of life.

In the early 1970s, psychologist Dr. Jay Weiss exposed two rats to the same stress—a mild shock to the tail—in a situation where only one of the rats had control of the stress. A third rat served as a comparison and was not shocked at all. The first rat learned that by rotating a wheel he could turn off the shock, both for himself and for the second rat. In this way both rats got exactly the same amount of stress, but the difference was that one rat could control the situation while the other was helpless. The helpless rats developed stomach ulcers twice as large as those of the rats that had control.

Unpredictability is closely related to uncontrollability. If rats were signaled with a beeping noise for ten seconds before the shock came on, they had much less severe ulcers. Knowing when to anticipate the stress allowed the rats to relax during the "safe" periods, reducing the wear and tear of chronic anxiety, which is really chronic fight-or-flight.

People who feel in control of life can withstand an enormous amount of change and thrive on it. People who feel helpless can hardly cope with change at all. Almost everyone knows people of both sorts. The truly imperturbable types might be represented by James Bond, because 007 is nothing if not stress-hardy. Bombs explode around him as he parachutes into the supervillain's diabolical nuclear reactor, but he calmly combs his hair and picks lint off his navy blazer. On the other hand, there are the emotionally fragile male protagonists in Woody Allen films. Insecure and awfulizing relentlessly about how bad things could get, Allen's characters are prone to develop ulcers when faced with what to order for dessert. The potential hazards of helplessness and emotional repression didn't escape Marshall Brickman and Woody Allen in their script of *Manhattan*. In it, Allen plays one of his typical retiring males. Diane Keaton, playing his girlfriend, announces that she is leaving Allen for his best friend. When the Allen character looks unperturbed, Keaton becomes agitated, demanding to know why he doesn't react. He sighs and tells her that he can't express anger. "I grow a tumor instead," he says.

Psychologist Martin Seligman, author of *The Optimistic Child*, points out that our ability to develop control begins in infancy, when the good mother mirrors and responds to the actions of her child. Baby smiles, mother smiles. Baby coos, mother coos. Baby cries with hunger, and mother responds with milk. Through this "dance of development," the infant learns that it has enough control to ensure its own survival.

Human infants raised in some institutionalized environments are deprived of this dance of development. They have no control since they are fed on schedule, are changed on schedule, and have little interaction with caretakers. Previously happy infants become weepy. After a few months they stop crying and become withdrawn, staring at the wall. At first they ignore people who approach them; later they begin to shriek. They lose weight, often develop insomnia, and are very prone to infections. Many die before they are three years old.

If no control is possible, then helplessness sets in. If your actions and responses don't make any difference, if you have no impact on the world, why bother? The person who has experienced helplessness in one situation is more likely to act helplessly in other situations. He or she has been conditioned.

Seligman contends that we learn to be helpless, and the resultant depressed behavior then feeds on itself. Helplessness is characterized by a decreased motivation to do anything about life's difficulties and by a negative mind-set that makes it hard to appreciate that you did something right when you actually do change a situation. Emotionally there is anxiety as long as you are trying to control an unpredictable situation, then depression and giving up when the situation seems beyond control.

Hardiness: Overcoming Helplessness

Life is filled with changes. It's whether we can cope with those changes or not that determines whether we will grow with the situation or be overcome by it, whether we will act helplessly or creatively. Psychologist Dr. Suzanne Ouellette (her name was Kobasa when the original work was published) and her colleagues, including Dr. Salvatore Maddi, studied the difference between these two extremes beginning with a landmark study published in 1979. In studies of business executives undergoing the stress of their company's divestiture, those who exhibited what the researchers dubbed a stress-hardy personality were far less likely to become ill than others who were less hardy to stress. The three factors that rendered people hardy in the face of stress all began with the letter C. The three C's are commitment, control, and challenge.

- *Commitment* is an attitude of curiosity and involvement with life. The situations that occur, the people interacted with, and the total environment of life are all sources of deep interest to those who exhibit commitment. These individuals stay involved with both tasks and relationships—they don't easily give up. If a conflict arises, they are more likely to inquire into it than to gloss over it. They have what has been called a "generalized sense of purpose" that encourages them to find meaning in life, and in their interactions and choices. The opposite of commitment is alienation—a feeling of separateness. At the extreme, think of the children in foundling homes who have withdrawn from the world and lack the capacity to relate to people or to the environment around them. A less extreme example might be the person who routinely takes the same walk and hardly ever sees anything new. The world is always changing, continually becoming new, and commitment is our capacity to engage meaningfully with that newness rather than to withdraw into a separate sense of self.
- *Control* is the opposite of helplessness. It is the predilection to think and feel that we can influence events, coupled with the willingness to act rather than be a victim of circumstances. Dr. Ouellette makes a very important point about control. It is not synonymous with the naive, and perennially popular, thought that we're omnipotent and can always create exactly the outcome we want. Rather, it's

the more mature understanding that we can make a positive difference in the world through what Dr. Ouellette refers to as exercising "imagination, knowledge, skill, and choice."

• *Challenge* is the belief that change is the essence of life, rather than maintenance of the status quo, and that in Dr. Ouellette's words, "Changes are interesting incentives to growth rather than threats to security."*

The attitudes of hardiness lead to a kind of coping that Ouellette and Maddi call *transformational*. Committed people who believe they are in control and expect life to be continuously in creative flux are likely to react to stressful events by *increasing* their interaction with them—exploring, engaging with, and learning from them. This attitude transforms the event into something less stressful by placing it in a broader frame of reference that revolves around continued personal growth and purpose in life.

Persons low in hardiness—and among those are people conditioned to be helpless—are likely to engage in what Ouelette calls *regressive coping*. Like the foundling home infants, regressive copers back away from stress and dwell instead on their own repetitive emotional reactions. They stay in a rut, are alienated from life, feel powerless to change things, and are therefore threatened by anything that rocks the boat. These people are the ones who are the most likely to fall ill when stressful events arise.

---

*Suzanne C. Kobasa, Salvatore R. Maddi, and Stephen Kahn, "Hardiness and Health: A Prospective Study," *Journal of Personality and Social Psychology*, 1982, 42(1): 168–177.

Psychiatrist George Vaillant, in a landmark study reported in his book *Adaptation to Life,* showed that mental health is the most important predictor of physical health. He analyzed data collected about the lives and the mental and physical health of a group of Harvard alumni over a period of thirty years. He found that men with immature coping styles, similar to regressive coping, became ill four times more often than men with hardier styles.

We are now beginning to understand some of the mechanisms underlying the erosion of health by poor coping. We are unraveling the intricate effect of chronic stress on hormones, neuropeptides, and the central nervous system, which in turn can affect every system of the body, from the immune to the cardiovascular. The effects of stress are buffered by effective coping and also by the love and support of other people. Vaillant found that lonely men often became chronically ill by the time they reached their fifties. It's only through our relationships to others that we develop the outlook of hardiness and come to believe in our own capabilities and inner goodness. The lonely baby is in no position to become hardy. The lonely adult may have problems sustaining the attitudes of hardiness.

In the 1950s, the small town of Roseto, Pennsylvania, raised considerable interest in the scientific community because of its strikingly low rate of death from coronary heart disease. Epidemiologists began to study the Rosetans, expecting to find low levels of the major risk factors for coronary heart disease: cigarette smoking, fat consumption, a sedentary lifestyle, and obesity. They got a big surprise. The Rosetans' health habits were no different from those of other Americans. They had similar risk factors. It turned out that the protective factor was actually the intimate social fabric of the community. The extended family was alive and well in this homogeneous Italian-American community. People tended to stay within Roseto, and so there was a great deal of closeness. People knew one another, their family histories, their joys and sorrows. In Roseto there were plenty of people to listen and to lend a hand when needed. In the 1960s, as Roseto became more Americanized and less close-knit, the rate and severity of heart attacks rose to the national level. In the 1990s the original researchers, using data from death certificates, conducted a fifty-year study of Rosetans, and confirmed their findings. Close family ties and a cohesive community turned out to be more important than health habits in predicting heart disease.

We've always known that we can literally die of broken hearts and shattered dreams. Laboratory findings are now corroborating that intuitive sense. The most pressing question for us, then, is how to reconnect with one another—how to develop the attitude of commitment that makes us curious about life and willing to engage deeply with other people, with our jobs, and with our own inner lives. How can we move under the surface of life and experience the fullness of its depths? And how can we do that in a way that is vital, fresh, and free—beyond the conditioning that so often causes us to close down in fear rather than open up in love?

At the heart of the process are the techniques we'll turn to in the next three chapters—meditation, breath control, and mindfulness—through which we can reach an internal balance point where the mind becomes still, balanced, and open. In the state of stillness, the physiology shifts into the relaxation response.

Negative conditioning circuits are derailed, and the mind is open to the formation of more productive habits.

In the coming chapters you will learn to reach that balance point, becoming aware of your own limiting mind habits and their effect on your body. You will be able to reduce or even prevent the automatic, conditioned responses that lead to stress and physical illness by creating new circuits that activate your own inner healing potential. You will learn the attitudes of stress hardiness—becoming more curious and present in the moment, and reframing life's stresses as challenges rather than as invitations to helplessness and defeat.

A side effect of this program of healing is a reconnection to the values that are most important in life: an openness to love, an attitude of forgiveness toward ourselves and others, and peace of mind. Without peace of mind, life is just a shadow of its limitless possibilities. The most beautiful landscape leaves you empty if your mind is full of worry. Even the arms of your beloved seem remote. One of my meditation teachers put it very clearly when he said that all the experiences of life are like zeros in a long number. They are meaningless without a digit in front of them. That digit is peace of mind.

Down with Guilt!

Over the years I've had many people tell me that they couldn't stop blaming themselves for getting sick. Or alternatively, friends and family were sometimes the source of blame. A patient of mine named Grace, who was a professor of psychology and a very bright and heartful woman, was convinced that getting breast cancer was entirely her own fault. She believed that she hadn't managed her stress well enough. John, who had developed multiple sclerosis, was convinced that, in his words, he had "juiced it" or attracted the disease to himself with his negative thinking. But things just aren't as simple as that.

In 1989 I had the opportunity to speak at the first Conference on Holistic Health and Medicine in Bangalore, India. Among the other speakers was His Holiness, the Dalai Lama. Much to my delight, the conference organizers wanted to make a video of an American woman and an Indian man interviewing His Holiness about the special perspectives that his Buddhist training might bring to understanding health and illness. I was graced by being the woman they chose. My very first question for His Holiness concerned what American philosopher Ken Wilber dubbed "New Age Guilt"—the naive idea that our thinking is totally responsible for our illness or other life circumstances.

His Holiness responded to my question about what to tell people who were suffering from such guilt with his trademark wisdom and good humor. He laughed and said something to the effect of "I would tell them not to be so simpleminded." Then he launched into an explanation very similar to the one I'm about to give you.

Although stress and anxiety can depress immune function, clearly we don't get sick each time we're frightened or tense, and some people can be chronically stressed for years and still stay healthy. It's far more reasonable to consider stress as one of many factors that may tip the balance toward illness. Each of the mechanisms I've discussed—the hormonal messengers linking the brain and the immune system, the fight-or-flight response, immunosuppression, and the relaxation response—function in bodies subject to three other important determinants of well-being: *heredity, environment,* and *behavior.*

Some people are constitutionally lucky; their genes are programmed for health and longevity. Others, less fortunate, are genetically predisposed to high blood pressure, heart disease, diabetes, multiple sclerosis, or certain cancers. Even so, many people with a possible genetically linked disease stay well. In my own case, exercise, diet, yoga, and the relaxation response buffered the genetic pattern of hyperarousal in my family that contributes to high blood pressure and migraines. For others, changing something in the environment such as diet can prevent the expression of migraines or hypertension or can alter the balance of the immune response.

The one factor that has links to every determinant of health, other than hardwired genetic constitution, is, of course, behavior. We decide about our health habits—whether we exercise, what we eat, whether we smoke or drink. Just as important, our minds have the ability to spin out endless imaginings that are quite real to the body. We can believe them or not. Although it would be a gross oversimplification to say that your thinking creates your health, it certainly plays a significant role. But remember that genetics, environment, and health habits are important—and often determining factors—in the equation. The good news is that regardless of what causes illness, learning to use your mind wisely can improve your health, reduce your stress, and help you to become a happier and more compassionate human being.

Ultimately, feeling guilty gives us a false sense of control: "If I can just eat this special diet, do this meditation, or affirm some-

thing more positive in my life, then I will heal." Although all of those things can indeed be helpful, none of them comes with a guarantee. As theologian Elaine Pagels once pointed out, from the beginning of time people have preferred guilt to helplessness. That way they can feel in control. Transformational coping—which really can have positive effects on health—means becoming mature and flexible enough to deal with life's inherent uncertainty. It doesn't mean that everything will always go the way that you hoped for. It means that you'll be able to grow in wisdom and compassion from every life circumstance.

Perhaps the greatest inspiration in my life is those patients who taught me that healing is more than curing. Although almost every person wants to be healthy, particularly when they've lost their health, the truth is that life is unpredictable. People with low stress, great health habits, and optimistic thinking still fall ill. Curing is great if we can get it, and thanks to allopathic medicine, integrative medicine, and the mind/body connection we have a lot of hope in that regard. But healing can happen even in the process of dying. I cannot tell you how many of my patients with cancer, AIDS, or other life-threatening diseases have told me that they wouldn't trade what they had learned about life and themselves even though they were facing death.

Ultimately minding the body and mending the mind have more to do with wholeness—healing—than with curing. To be whole means to be a flexible adventurer, ready to meet life's challenges with engagement and curiosity. It means feeling a sense of connection to the whole of life—to other people, to new ideas, to the world around us. It means thinking less about "I, me, and mine" and more about how we are all interconnected in a great

web of life. It means caring for others and doing what we can to make the world a better place. It means recognizing that happiness arises within us *independent* of any external cause and removing the obstructions to that inner peace and happiness that are our birthright as human beings.

Whether you are healthy or sick, young or old, rich or poor, you can still be happy and optimize your physical function. That's what minding the body and mending the mind are all about.

CHAPTER 2

Getting Back in Control

The paradox of control is simple. The more we try to control life, the less control we have. One summer I watched an adorable little boy, about four years old, playing at the beach. He had built a sand castle with a moat around it when the tide was out. As the tide moved in, a wave would occasionally break close enough for some water to trickle into the moat and fill it. The child was delighted his invention worked. But as the tide continued to rise, the waves lapped at the castle, threatening destruction. The child began frantically to pile up sand in front of the castle, building a dike to deflect the flood. He was caught in a constant struggle of breaking down and building up.

Several yards down the beach, a girl of about the same age began a parallel struggle, but not for long. She soon recognized the inevitability of the tide and moved on to a game of digging holes at the tide line, watching them fill with water and erode. As the tide rose and each hole filled, she moved back and started her game anew. The first child ended up angry and frustrated: His castle had been destroyed in spite of every effort to control the tides. The second child had instead discovered a new game and spent a doubly pleasant afternoon. She had both literally and figuratively learned to go with the flow—to let go.

Not knowing when to let go, throwing useless effort into protecting sand castles, is a major cause of stress and loss of creativity. As we saw in Chapter 1, feeling that we're in control is primary to health. On the other hand, if we try to control too tightly, we're likely to wind up like the little boy on the beach. How to resolve this paradox? Developing the discrimination to tell when to hold on and when to let go is key to escaping past conditioning and responding freshly to life's challenges. This means being flexible and self-aware. The Japanese say that in a storm, it is the bamboo, the flexible tree, that can bend with the wind and survive. The rigid tree that resists the wind falls, victim of its own insistence to control.

Stress as Opportunity

It's hard to know how well we'll manage until we're handed an invitation to stress. Shakespeare said, "When the sea was calm all boats alike showed mastership in floating." Only in a storm are they obliged to cope. Storms and struggles, chaos and tragedy, have always been looked upon as the teachers of valuable, if initially unwelcome, lessons. In the struggle to survive a stressful situation, a new way of being often emerges that's much more satisfying than the old. Every religion and the great myths and fables of all cultures discuss change and growth through the archetypes of death and rebirth. Easter and Passover, symbolic of death and resurrection, are also metaphors for escape from our past conditioning and outmoded concepts—and rebirth into freedom. The phoenix that arises from its own ashes and the seed that dies to give birth to the flower are all variations on the theme of life as a continuous process of growth. An endless round of little deaths and rebirths.

Why, then, do we hold onto the old so earnestly? What is the block to letting go in the moment? That block is fear: lack of faith in ourselves and in life. If I give up a bad relationship, maybe no one better will come along. If I look for a new job, maybe I'll get a worse one. If I let go of my suspicion, maybe I'll be hurt and disappointed by people. It's fear that masquerades as the need to control, and fear that deprives us of the chance to be free.

Most Americans don't like to think about pain and suffering. We are an optimistic people, inclined to think of the future as unfolding with endless promise. Usually we avoid pain until it hurts enough so that it can no longer be ignored. Buddhist philosophy revolves around the inevitability of suffering in human life. The first of the Four Noble Truths states quite simply that life is suffering (unsatisfactory). The other truths discuss how attitudes create suffering, and they pave the way for understanding how those attitudes can be changed.

The process of facing change in a stress-hardy manner by allowing it to be an opportunity rather than a threat can be accomplished by anyone who wants to learn. Here is how to begin.

Step 1: Willing to Be Aware
My mother once assured me that ignorance is bliss. What you don't think about can't hurt you. This coping style is popular

indeed, but it's a great description of regressive coping, which ensures stress and prevents engaging with—and even enjoying—the changes that life inevitably brings.

People do the best they can to get through life comfortably. No normal person knowingly creates suffering. The walls of protection that we build against awareness of our suffering seem like a good idea. The trouble is that they keep us prisoners of our own misconceptions. Children are often frightened in the dark because they mistake harmless things, like the shadow of a shirt hanging over the back of a chair, for horrible monsters. Some have the courage to turn on the light and have a look. They're the lucky ones. Others can at least cry out for help, and they, too, become free of their illusions. But those who choose to hide under the covers, afraid even to breathe, are in the worst position of all. They are prisoners of their own imagination.

When we grow older, it's not so easy to hide under the covers. Instead, we learn to hide from ourselves, from our own frightening thoughts and feelings. This is most easily accomplished by distraction: learning to ignore bad feelings by thinking of other things. Some people get so good that they can't remember the frightening feelings at all. Such denial is the cradle in which fear grows up. Fear makes your body tense. The mind responds by producing conditioned mental associations to tension. Thus, the types of distracting thoughts that form most likely will be worries and fears over other things.

One of my patients, a woman named Nancy, had a terrible marriage, but she couldn't admit it to herself. Her husband was an alcoholic. He was often withdrawn and sullen, rarely reaching out lovingly to her and their children. Nancy had long ago stopped talking to him about his drinking, since he'd call her a nag and denounce her as the one with the problem.

Nonetheless, they still cared for each other. She felt powerless and scared, but she rationalized her situation, hiding her true feelings. When we talked about her husband, at first she said he didn't drink *that* much. He was a pretty good father, a respectable professional, and really a sweet person at heart. They had been married for twenty years, much longer than many of their friends. She had pushed her fear and anger down very deep, which takes a lot of energy. This is denial, the psychic equivalent of pulling the covers over your head. The price she paid was a state of chronic tension that showed up in two ways: physically as headaches, nausea, and insomnia, and psychologically as compulsive behavior.

Nancy, who looked tired and aged beyond her forty-five years, was constantly concerned about her teenage children. They were great kids, but an unending parade of "what ifs" ran through her mind like squirrels. What if they got into a car accident, what if they got into drugs, what if they got mugged, raped, disappointed, sick, and so forth without stop. She couldn't turn off the worries when she lay down to sleep, so sleep became a serious problem. She tried to control all her children's comings and goings. It was only her physical ills that finally made her reach out for help and open up to an understanding of how her regressive coping was costing her both her health and her peace of mind. Then she could learn what it means to really have control—to take responsibility for her marriage.

Worry shows up both mentally and physically—a perfect setup for the creation of a vicious cycle. Worried thoughts, whether conscious or repressed like Nancy's, create tension through the physiology of the fight-or-flight response. Physical tension narrows our mental focus and we tend to worry more. The cycle becomes self-sustaining. It's possible to worry about anything at all. Advanced worriers spend little time worrying about current problems. Instead, they choose from the endless buffet of past memories and future fantasies. Some become superstitious, with worrying becoming a talisman that prevents bad things from happening. It's awfully tiring to be scouting endlessly for danger, since our minds can create new dangers out of thin air. Awareness of our fears is the first step toward breaking out of the pattern of worry and overcontrol. Step 2 is changing the mind-set that is conditioned to fear and freeing the innate healing power within you.

Step 2: Freeing the Inner Physician

Life naturally tends toward wholeness and growth. Even the inhospitable cracks in city sidewalks sustain seeds that will do their best to sprout, no matter what the conditions. When our energy is tied up in useless worry and fight-or-flight, though, we oppose the natural tendency toward growth and wholeness. This is where the relaxation response comes in.

Its physiology is in itself healing, creating a state of lowered arousal of the sympathetic nervous system, the fight-or-flight system, that diminishes many symptoms caused by or worsened by stress. The action of the relaxation response is twofold. Like a prescription drug, it has a direct effect on the body and it has certain side effects. These side effects result from an awareness that helps us break through our conditioning.

Meditation is a way both to access the relaxation response and to become aware of the mind and how our attitudes produce stress. This capacity to observe our own minds leads to stress hardiness. By provoking questioning about life's meanings, it develops a curiosity about things that leads to a deeper engagement with life—an attitude of *commitment*. By teaching the mind to become aware and then to let go, meditation trains us in responsibility and appropriate *control*. By allowing the emergence of new attitudes, we develop the understanding that life's apparent threats are *challenges* to growth.

In addition to building stress hardiness, meditation also releases the inner physician by quieting the mind so that the body's own inner wisdom can be heard. My former husband, Miroslav, tells a story of immigrating to this country when he was about seven years old. Shortly after arriving, a girl of five made a beeline for an orange stand. She ate three or four oranges in a few minutes—a prodigious snack for such a small child. The little girl had obviously endured physical and emotional conditions on her long trip that created a need for vitamin C. Scientists have long known that children whose appetites have not been dulled by sugar and rich, fatty foods will choose a perfectly balanced diet. This is the wisdom of the body.

At other times the body may need exercise, rest, or physical touch. When the body's inner wisdom is obscured by inattention through worry, the result is similar to having the appetite dulled by sweets: We can't hear the prescription of the inner healer. Meditation, through its ability to help us quiet the mind, restores that ability of inner listening, allowing us to make the healthiest, most creative choices.

When most of us tune in to the mind, listening to what passes through, we become aware of an insistent internal conversation with ourselves. That inner dialogue is the endless stream of thinking that comments on our experiences. We are often more tuned in to its commentary than we are to what's actually happening, with the result that we miss the moment. We live in endless variations of old reruns of the mind. If we were once frightened in a dark alley, we may always feel fright in dark alleys, even if there's no cause. As soon as the mind sees the alley, it reruns old tapes of fear and doubt. Regardless of reality, fear and doubt are what we feel. Because the storehouse of our past experience is so large, the inner dialogue has endless material out of which to shape a description of the world.

Do you ever have trouble remembering someone's name right after you're introduced? Most people do. Instead of paying attention to the person's name, you think about things like what you will say, whether you're standing close enough to offend him with the garlic from last night's antipasto, whether she will like you, whether you will like her, how big his nose is, what color her clothes are, and so forth in endless variation. This thinking goes on without our complete awareness; you are "lost in thought" and are not "present" with what's actually going on, so you miss the name.

We all experience many such moments. We fly by the highway exit before we can notice it, or we stand in front of the refrigerator and can't remember why. We're literally out to lunch—and sadly it's often in a proverbial garbage heap of worries, fears, blame, and doubts.

The first step toward becoming conscious is learning to become aware of the constantly changing landscape of thoughts, feelings, and perceptions that constipate the mind and mask awareness of the inner physician. Lost in the inner dialogue, we're only partly awake, sleepwalking our way through life.

To develop a state of inner awareness, to witness and let go of the old dialogues, you need an observation point. If you went out in a boat to view offshore tides but neglected to put down an anchor, you would soon be carried off to sea. So it is with the mind. Without an anchor to keep the mind in place, it will be carried away by the torrent of thoughts. Your ability to watch what is happening will be lost. The practice of meditation, which calms the body through the relaxation response and fixes the mind through dropping the anchor of attention, is the most important tool of self-healing and self-regulation.

Meditation Is Being Here Now

Think of an activity that you really enjoy. Perhaps it's a hot summer day and you're walking through the woods toward a small lake situated like a sparkling emerald in a verdant meadow. The wildflowers and tall grasses create a magnificent tapestry of living texture and color. The wind is fragrant as it gently ruffles your hair and cools you off. Wading slowly into the lake, savoring each step, you finally dive in, seemingly one with the indescribable, subtle essence of the clear, pure water. Ahh. For a moment the world stops. No longer concerned with work, bills, shopping, relationships, or any other thoughts, you experience complete surrender. That's what enjoyment is. You're in the moment.

One of my patients named Sally had lost interest in her sex life, because she'd forgotten how to be present in the moment. I asked her what went on in her mind during lovemaking. Sally told me that she and her husband made love on Saturday mornings, and her mind was usually making a list of the day's events. She worked all week and Sunday was the time for church and family visits, so Saturday was the day for shopping, cleaning, and other errands. Since her mind was at the dry cleaner's, there was no one home to enjoy the sex!

To get back to a good sex life, Sally had to become aware of the causes of her problem: the time she and her husband had chosen and the way her mind reacted. She addressed both by taking action to change their "date" time and by retraining her mind through meditation, in learning to surrender, to let go to the experience. *These two paths—taking action where required and surrendering when no further action is possible—are paths to stress hardiness.*

Since all of us have natural periods of focused concentration—like when we're balancing a checkbook or watching a sporting event—the state of meditation is actually quite familiar. It occurs whenever we're fully engaged in what we're doing. In all those cases, a shift occurs between what's in the foreground and what's in the background of the mind. Think about how you feel when you're really in the present moment with something. It may be skiing, swimming, reading a good book, making love, planting flowers—anything that holds your attention. *Take a minute and remember this feeling.* Peaceful and focused, right?

For once, the mind isn't running through the list of things that *must* happen before you can be happy. It's not reciting the list of awful things that *could* happen to steal your happiness. It has taken a backseat to *just being.* This is the meditative state that elicits the relaxation response. It is alert, peaceful presence. As we'll discuss further in Chapter 4, the presence that we're all looking for is there all the time. The problem is that we can't appreciate it as long as our minds are in turmoil. *Here is the big secret.* External things—sex, food, even natural beauty—don't create peace and happiness. They focus the mind to reveal what's already inside you. Imagine a precious pearl lying at the bottom of a shallow pond. When the water is calm, the pearl is visible. When the water is agitated, it's obscured. But it's always there, waiting for the silt to settle. That's what meditation does: It allows the silt to settle.

Learning to meditate is like learning to do anything. The first requirement is motivation. Without it, there's no energy to make the effort. For most of us, this is no problem. Stress, pain, suffering, no peace of mind—these adverse circumstances become opportunities because they lead to making changes. The second requirement is effort. You have to practice in order to learn. Reading a dozen books isn't worth a week's practice. At a minimum, ten to twenty minutes per day are required to start getting the hang of meditation. The third requirement is determination. People often quit activities when they decide that they'll never be any good at them. Meditation is no exception. Because you're zeroing in on your mind, what you'll notice at first is its turbulence, as well as its moments of peace. If you interpret the turbulence as "I can't do this," your mind has won by using one of its favorite tricks, which you'll read about in Chapter 6.

I remember learning to jog. I was very out of shape. Ten years of heavy smoking had taken a toll on my lungs. Furthermore, I came from a family in which no one had ever heard of exercise;

our idea of cardiovascular fitness was to increase the heart rate by drinking coffee and smoking cigarettes! At first, jogging was torture. Every step was proof I wasn't cut out for exercise. I was sustained, however, by the memory of a PBS program that featured an older woman who had learned to jog and now ran forty miles a week. She had started by running to her mailbox and back—a few yards. Next, she jogged on the street, then walked until she recovered her breath. In a couple of months she could jog a mile, then two miles, until she got all the way up to eight miles at a time.

I was impressed. I was younger and a lot thinner. I had no excuses. As I jogged, my lungs would burn and my legs ache. My mind would say, "I told you, Joan, all Zakons [my maiden name] have small lungs; you will never do this." I had a secret weapon, however, because I knew how to meditate and win the battle of the mind by ignoring it. On every in breath I repeated the phrase "If she can do it," and on every out breath I repeated "so can I." And I could. After a few months, even out-of-shape I could run for five miles.

Remember, *when practicing, just do it; don't get discouraged.* It took years for your mind to build its scaffolding of tricks and worries. It will take time to dismantle them. *Don't evaluate your performance.* Like the beginning jogger, you should think, "Great—I did it." Not "It was a great jog" or a rotten jog. It was a jog. That's enough.

You already know that meditation is nothing more than anchoring your attention in the present. That's exactly what I was doing in the jogging example. Instead of becoming lost in my mind's complaints, I focused on breathing. Breathing is a neutral focus that is with us every moment of the day. Breathing is an anchor, or focus, common to many traditional forms of meditation. To anchor the mind even more firmly, a word or phrase is often added, repeated silently in time to the breathing. "If she can do it . . . so can I" is a good example of a focus phrase, used in meditation. These—like mantras, which are sacred words or sounds like *Om*—are like brooms, sweeping the mind clear of other thoughts.

Focus words can be neutral, meaningless sounds, or meaningful phrases. In Dr. Herbert Benson's book, *Beyond the Relaxation Response: The Faith Factor,* he writes about the power of a person's belief and how it can support the practice of meditation. When Dr. Benson surveyed world literature, both secular and nonsecular, for instructions on meditation, he found a traditional Japanese approach that used counting as a focus. You breathe in and out on the count of one. On the next breath you move to two and so forth until you get to ten. Then you count back down to one over the next ten breaths.

When Dr. Benson tried this in a laboratory experiment with student volunteers, he got an unexpected result. The students became so flustered when they repeatedly lost count that they couldn't elicit the relaxation response. All he was able to measure was their performance anxiety. He told them to forget counting and just stick with the word *one*. Breathe in, breathe out, and repeat *one* on each out breath. That worked fine, and he was able to document the physiological effects of meditation.

The same word, though, won't be appropriate for everyone. Take my first patient. Alan, a computer company executive, came to the clinic to learn the relaxation response to counteract the nausea and vomiting of the chemotherapy he was receiving for cancer. We both shut our eyes and I had him relax his body. I instructed him to just follow his breathing, repeating the word *one* on each out breath. After a few minutes of this, I could hear that he was breathing faster than before, and when I opened my eyes to check on him, I could see that his facial muscles were tense. I gently stopped the meditation and asked him what was happening. He then told me that the number *one* was the logo of his company and that thinking about it made him anxious over missed work, his illness, and many other things. So he chose a different focus, one that evoked a sense of peacefulness, and he was finally able to let go.

Some people prefer a neutral sound. For them the word *one* may be just fine. Sounds with *mmm* and *nnn* evoke pleasant associations like letting go and enjoyment. Other people prefer a phrase with meaning like *peace, trust,* or *let go.* Still others use a few words or a phrase from a prayer—either a familiar prayer or a prayer that comes spontaneously from the heart.

When I was still running the Mind/Body Clinic, one patient chose the focus "Dearest Lord" on the in breath and "I surrender to your grace" on the out breath. The peace that was generated as she meditated with that focus was palpable in the room. The power and beauty of her faith were magnified by making God her single focus. This is the reason for the religious use of meditation. Thoughts of God, when brought to the forefront, are much more powerful than when mixed into the background of daily concerns. The use of meditation in sports or creativity training is similar. The greatest connection to the task at hand can be made with a concentrated mind.

Some Eastern forms of meditation have traditionally employed mantras—sounds or words with spiritual meaning. For instance, the sacred sound *Om* has the same meaning as *The Word* in Christianity. It refers to the primordial sound, or vibration, from which the universe was created. Physicists might say it is the sound of the echo of the Big Bang. Neurophysiologists might say it's a good word for meditation because it entrains the mind in associations of pleasant things—*mmm* is the prototype of enjoyment.

The choice of a focus word is a matter for contemplation. If you have religious beliefs, you might like to choose a word or phrase from your own tradition. If you don't, then you might choose either a neutral focus or something personally meaningful. One very tense patient I remember chose an affirmation to remind him of his intention to shift his priorities so that he could reduce his stress. He repeated *my* on the in breath and *time* on the out breath.

If you can't think of a focus, you might want to try a traditional Sanskrit mantra, *Ham Sah*. It's supposed to mimic the sound of the incoming and outgoing breath. It's called a natural mantra because it goes on day and night without stop. One needs only to tune into it. *Ham* means "I am" and *Sah* means "that." *That* is regarded as the part of the mind that witnesses all our experience—or awareness itself. We'll explore that topic in depth in Chapter 4. If you're religious, you can imagine this indwelling awareness as your connection to God. If you're not religious, you can think of it just as awareness, as the power of the mind to come to balance through the act of self-observation.

The Process of Meditation

1. **Choose a quiet spot where you won't be disturbed by other people or by the telephone.** This extends to animals as well. In-evitably, if you have a dog or a cat, it will find a way into your space, so arrange to put your pet in another room.

Many of us are used to being at the beck and call of the world; this is one time you're not. *This is time you're giving to yourself.* If you don't take time to recharge, always putting other things first, you can't be authentically happy, nor will you make others happy.

We had a rule about meditation in our house when the kids were growing up: Do not disturb unless there's blood involved. It's as simple as that. *This is your time:* Time you take for yourself to more fully understand the interaction of your mind, body, and spirit. Time you take to recharge and to be present to life itself, a miracle that often goes unappreciated.

2. **Sit in a comfortable but balanced position**, with back straight and arms and legs uncrossed, unless you choose to sit cross-legged on a floor cushion. Lift yourself up from your hips, so that your spine feels long and graceful. Now imagine that you're tucking a pair of wings against your back. Your chest will open so that your breathing can be full and relaxed.

3. **Close your eyes**. This makes it easier to concentrate at first. But if you're more comfortable with your eyes open, there are two basic choices: You can keep your eyes relaxed and down-cast—at half-mast, as I like to put it—and focus on a neutral

our own out breath? Every out breath is an opportunity to let go and relax.

Now that you've got a sense of how to relax by letting go as you breathe out, you can consciously do this with your whole body. Starting with your forehead, become aware of any tension there as you breathe in. Let go of any obvious tension as you breathe out, just as you did with your shoulders. Go through the rest of your body in this way, proceeding down through your eyes, jaws, neck, shoulders, arms, hands, chest, upper back, middle back and midriff, lower back, belly, pelvis, buttocks, thighs, calves, and feet. This need only take a minute or two. And you'll get much better at it as you practice. Noticing your major muscle groups, and letting them relax, is one of the most pleasant and interesting sensations that you'll ever experience. So just be curious about what you're feeling. Tune into it and enjoy.

5. **Stay aware of your breathing.** You're breathing all the time, aware of it or not. You don't so much breathe as you are automatically breathed. In the next chapter we'll take up breath control as a shortcut to eliciting the relaxation response. For the purpose of meditation, however, *let the breath happen by itself.* You may notice that your breathing gets slower and shallower as the meditation progresses. That's due to the physiological effects of the relaxation response, the fact that your body requires less oxygen because your metabolism has slowed down.

6. **Repeat your focus word silently in time to your breathing.** You may have chosen a word or phrase to repeat just on the out

spot a few feet in front of you. Or you can open and
eyes—focusing on either the sky or the horizon. Thi
especially conducive to engaging with a larger perspe
feels intimate and inclusive but doesn't stimulate
about your personal situation.

4. Relax your muscles sequentially from head to fo
step helps to break the connection between stressful tl
and a tense body. Here's how to get the hang of relaxii
muscles. Take a moment right now to practice. We'll u:
shoulders as an example of how every body part can b
sciously released in tune with your out breath:

- Imagine that an umbrella is inflating in your belly
  breathe in and then folding up as you breathe out. Or
  ine that a bird is opening its graceful wings in your b
  you breathe in and closing its wings as you breathe ou

- Once you're able to focus on the breath coming ii
  going out as a physical sensation of expansion and l
  go, focus on letting your shoulders relax on the out br
  They should relax downward noticeably.

- Take a few more breaths and notice how your shoul
  continue to relax and move down as you breathe out
  the conscious intention to let your shoulder muscles g

The pull of gravity is always present, encouraging you to
go, but if there's no awareness of being uptight, there can't be
letting go. Notice your shoulders again as you read on. Is th
any room to release them further, cooperating with gravity a

breath, or you may have a phrase that is broken up, part on the in breath and part on the out breath. In the case of *Ham Sah,* just listen to your breath, imagining that it sounds like *Ham* on the in breath and *Sah* on the out breath.

7. Don't worry about how you're doing. As soon as you start to worry about whether you're doing it right, you've shifted from meditation to anxiety. Without doubt, you'll do this a lot at first; it's just the habit of the mind to question and criticize our own performance. If you notice that tendency, try labeling it *judging,* then let go, coming back to the breath and the focus, which are your anchors in the shifting tides of the mind.

Your mind won't stop for more than seconds at a time at first, so don't expect it to. What happens is that you, that part of yourself that can watch or witness the shenanigans of the mind, is learning to flex its muscles. Each time you notice that you've drifted into thought, try labeling where you were—for instance, *"thinking, thinking"* or *"anger, anger"* or *"judging, judging"*—and then let it go, getting back to the anchor. In this way, you begin to train your mind in awareness—the antidote to denial and mental unconsciousness. The awareness you develop in meditation will begin to carry over into life, affording you much more choice in how you respond and enhancing your ability to enjoy life. In meditation there are two basic choices: to keep observing the train of thought as a detached witness or to let go and come back to the breath. Inevitably, you will do both.

The most common experience and complaint about meditation is "I can't stop my mind from wandering." That's fine. Don't try. Just practice bringing it back whenever you notice it wandering. St. Francis de Sales had a great comment about wandering thoughts: You can't stop the birds from flying back and forth over your head, but you can stop them from nesting in your hair. Try to do just that. Let the thoughts come and go as if they were birds passing across the blue sky of a clear mind. The clear blue that you will perceive when the thoughts slow down is peace. Peace of mind.

8. **Practice at least once a day for ten to twenty minutes.** Remember that practice is indispensable to progress at anything. In meditation the session itself is your only goal. In the truest sense, the process is the product. Your aim is to sit and meditate. Even if it seems that the only thing you're doing is chasing after your mind and occasionally remembering to come back to the breath, remarkably the relaxation response is still most likely occurring. Long before you think you "know how to do it," you will begin to notice that you're generally feeling more peaceful and that stress-related physical symptoms are beginning to improve. Although there is no goal to reach, it gets easier to stay focused after repeated practice.

If you can sit twice a day for ten to twenty minutes, so much the better. The preferred times are early morning before breakfast or before dinner. The only times to avoid are when you're tired, simply because meditation is a concentration exercise (and, if you're tired, you'll fall asleep), and just after a heavy meal, since the process of digestion makes people sluggish.

Reread the instructions and meditate for
ten or twenty minutes before reading any further.

The Experience of Meditation

Beginning meditators have one or more of three basic experiences: relaxation, sleep, or anxiety. Let's take a close look at each of them as you review the experience of your own meditation.

Relaxation

Most people experience at least a few minutes of relaxation during meditation. It's easy to understand why. At those moments when the mind takes a backseat and the inner dialogue slows down, what's left is the experience of just being in the present. Even when that experience is simply watching the breath and repeating a focus, it brings about a sense of relaxation and peacefulness because that state is what our basic nature actually is. We experience peace whenever the mind slows down. Since we can't always participate in skiing, gardening, or whatever favorite activity slows our minds and thus gives us peace, meditation becomes a portable minivacation. It can always be experienced. As we'll see in the next chapters, meditation need not be confined to ten- or twenty-minute periods. It can be practiced for a minute or a few minutes anytime during the day. Furthermore, any activity can be engaged in as if it were meditation. *The final goal of meditation is to become awake—here and now—so that conscious choice and peace of mind become the norm rather than the exception.*

Sleep or Drowsiness

Learning is a matter of association. When you close your eyes with the intention of letting go, sleep is the conditioned response that the body knows best. In fact, sleep can't come until you let go, which is why worrying or excitement often results in insomnia. Therefore, it's common to fall asleep or at least become drowsy when you first learn to meditate. The way to avoid that is to keep a straight back and not get too comfortable. Unless you have a physical problem that makes it impossible to meditate in a sitting position, don't meditate lying down. This definitely invites sleep. With time, the body becomes reconditioned so that sleep isn't an automatic response to letting go when you close your eyes. It becomes progressively easier to maintain a state of relaxed concentration.

If you have trouble falling asleep at night, however, then meditating while lying down is a great idea. Most people find that meditation is a powerful aid to falling asleep and to sleeping more soundly. Even if you're generally asleep within minutes of hitting the pillow, it's a good idea to meditate for even a short time because your sleep becomes more restful.

The sleep state is variable. Everyone has had the experience of sleeping for eight hours and awakening completely rested on most occasions but exhausted on others. Part of the variation has to do with what happens during periods of rapid-eye-movement, or REM, sleep, when you're dreaming. Since the body can't distinguish what is actually happening from what is imagined either during dreams or when awake, your body tells the tale of what happened in the dream state. If your dreams are restless, tense, or disturbing, they will affect how rested you feel upon awakening.

Never go to sleep listening to radio talk shows or television. It's bad enough to have to contend with what your own mind manufactures without adding the negative fantasies and opinions of other people. As we'll discuss in Chapter 4, the conscious and unconscious minds are very close together at the time of falling asleep, as they are during meditation, and you're particularly open to disturbing (or inspirational) influences at those times. Protect yourself by going to sleep peacefully. If you need a calming influence, try listening to restful music.

If you awaken during the night, meditate—don't ruminate! Counting sheep, you probably recognize by now, is a form of meditation. Meditating for regular periods during the day builds the mental muscles of letting go, making it easier to call on them when you need to focus the mind and stop thinking so that you can fall asleep. About half the people who came to the Mind/Body Clinic when I was the director had sleep disturbances. Either they had trouble falling asleep, had trouble staying asleep, or woke up too early in the morning and couldn't get back to sleep. A significant number of them found that their sleep improved after just a few weeks of meditation practice.

If you're troubled by insomnia, there are a few hints to keep in mind. First, gradually give up caffeine—especially after 3 p.m. You may be surprised at the rapid improvement in your sleep. Second, don't ever use alcoholic beverages to make you drowsy so that you can get to sleep. A few hours after ingesting alcohol, there's a rebound phase of excitement of the sympathetic nervous system, very similar to a fight-or-flight response. This shift in the nervous system often awakens people with a feeling of anxiety and restlessness. Third, if you wake up at night and can't get back to sleep within fifteen minutes, get up and meditate. Some of the early experiments that Dr. Benson performed showed that the body's metabolism, as measured by oxygen consumption, drops further during a twenty-minute meditation than it does during eight hours of sleep. The restful, hypometabolic physiology of the relaxation response will substitute for at least some of the lost sleep, and you'll feel much better the next day.

Catnappers may also find that ten to twenty minutes of meditation are a better battery recharger than thirty to sixty minutes of napping. Try it out and see what works for you.

Anxiety

About one-third to one-half of all new meditators become anxious during some part of meditation. The reason is simple. Meditation is a time when you're left alone with your own mind. There are no distractions. All the worries that you may be trying to escape by keeping busy have the opportunity to flood in and vie for your attention. I call this the anxiety parade. It may vary, from the common "laundry list" experience of rerunning all the things you have to do, to the sudden realization of the things you haven't yet done (forgotten phone calls and the like), to more deep-seated problems. Some people call the anxiety parade boredom because it's a familiar mental habit. But if you stop to inquire into what the experience of boredom is like, it will often reveal an underlying anxiety.

If you take the position of observing the worries, as St. Francis de Sales suggested, just letting them fly in and out without letting them "nest in your hair," then the anxiety parade will wind down. Like an insistent child who tugs on your coattails for attention, your mind has to be gently reminded that this is the time for letting go instead of holding on, and it will soon make the new association and slow down.

The most universal reason for experiencing anxiety during meditation is performance anxiety. Nearly everyone gets involved in deciding that they're doing it wrong. People worry over the tendency of the mind to wander, but nothing could be more natural than noticing the ongoing inner dialogue. *The primary goal of meditation is not relaxation—it is awareness. This is what leads eventually to getting the mind back under control. Relaxation is a side effect of learning how to meditate.* Therefore, a restless meditation is usually a better learning experience than one where the mind becomes peaceful. In time the mind will slow down as you build the facility of becoming aware and making the choice to let go.

Meditation is a form of mental martial arts. It's not that the mind stops attacking, but that you learn to take a different stance toward the attack. If you start to berate yourself for being restless, you've picked up the invitation of your mind to do battle, and battle is what you'll experience, as tension and anxiety. Instead, learn to adopt the stance of the aikido student. Move gracefully aside and let thoughts speed by without engaging them in a struggle. In that way, your mind will tire itself out as you hold the centered position of witnessing your own thoughts.

The process of meditation is similar to that of trying to balance your checkbook with the television turned on. At first you're into adding up the checks, concentrating on the task at hand. Then something loud occurs on the TV, maybe a commercial. For a moment it grabs your attention. You get involved in the show. Sooner or later you say, "Wait a minute, I'm supposed to be balancing my checkbook," and you let go of the TV and surrender once again to the checkbook. This dance of going back and forth may continue for quite some time. So it is with the process of meditation. When you finish balancing the books, you won't say, "What a lousy checkbook balancer I am—I keep getting distracted." Instead, it's more likely that you will be pleased at having completed the task. It's the same with meditation. *Remember, the only definition of a good meditation is one that you did.*

Since meditation is a process of awareness, you'll become progressively more tuned in to what goes on in your mind. At times old memories and long-forgotten incidents may reveal themselves. Some of these may be disturbing. That's natural and good. Consider it analogous to how the body rids itself of a splinter. At first the splinter causes pain, but if it's too deep to remove, soon the body becomes insensitive to it. Similarly, when something painful happens that you can't work out at the time, the experience will recede deeper into your unconscious. This is the mechanism of repression. Sooner or later the body will mount a response to the splinter, and an irritation will develop around it and then an infection. The resulting infection will cause some pressure and pain, but in the process the buried splinter will be lifted to the surface and finally expelled. In meditation the splinters of the mind will also work themselves to the surface with time, where you become aware of them and can finally take action in resolving the cause of the discomfort. In some cases you'll have to take some action, as Nancy did in confronting her alcoholic husband and then getting professional help to heal from her own pattern of codependency. In other cases the action you take will be letting go. In the succeeding chapters we'll explore more fully how to use the awareness that meditation creates.

SUGGESTIONS FOR THE READER

1. Meditate daily, once or preferably twice, for ten to twenty minutes each time.

2. Set aside a special place in your home for meditation. Remember, the mind learns by association. When you sit down at the dinner table, you probably experience hunger, salivation, and other eating-related responses before the meal actually comes. When you sit down in your TV chair, your mind immediately sinks into a receptive state of watching. When you stand in front of your clothes closet, your "time-to-get-dressed" program takes over so that you can move efficiently. It's the same with meditation. The place where you habitually meditate takes on the energy of that activity. Many people find that whenever they enter their meditation space, they feel a sense of peace even if they don't sit down at that time.

   Your place of meditation can be any corner, or a room if you have the space, where you don't do anything else. Make it pleasing and restful. Some people enjoy decorating the area with special pictures or plants or objects that are meaningful. Your meditation chair or cushion is best reserved for only that activity. Since you'll be sitting still for ten to twenty minutes, your position is very important. You should feel comfortable and well balanced. Soft chairs are generally the least comfortable because they provide inadequate support. A hard chair with a straight back will be the most comfortable kind of seat. You may want to put a cushion behind your lower back to keep your spine straight, which will help you sit comfortably and reduce the possibility of falling asleep.

Since you'll be still for an extended period, you may start to feel chilly even though your skin temperature warms during meditation. It's good to have a sweater or shawl to wrap yourself in so that physical discomfort will be less likely to distract you. *Remember, this is time that you take for yourself. Let your family know that it's important to you so that they'll respect your meditation.*

3. Remember not to judge your performance. In fact, try not to judge anything in meditation. At its best, meditation is a state of nonjudgmental awareness. Let your judge and censor rest for a while. It's a real relief.

CHAPTER 3

Breaking the Anxiety Cycle

Roger, a twenty-seven-year-old division manager for a high-tech firm, suffered with two related problems: high blood pressure and a fear of public speaking. Roger's blood pressure had been elevated for about two years, almost precisely as long as he had worked in his current job. Labeled a rising star, he'd moved up quickly through the managerial ranks, compulsively trying to stay in control of all possible situations.

He arrived ten minutes early for our first consultation. I had a brief errand to run and caught sight of him as I left my office. He was perched at the edge of his chair, his right leg bouncing up and down, while he quickly leafed through a magazine article. After a short delay in the medical records office, I was five minutes late for our appointment. Was he mad!

During the course of Roger's appointment, he continued to play beat the clock. He was aggressive, often hostile and confrontational. Roger was so restless that he was in motion even while sitting; his leg bounced and he constantly shifted positions. He looked like a tiger ready to pounce. His bodily tension was mirrored by mental tension. Roger could think of six things at the same time—phone calls, dinner plans, appointments—and frequently tried to take care of them all at once, multitasking to the max.

Physiological research indicates that people like Roger have a more reactive sympathetic nervous system, the fight-or-flight system, than less competitive people. The heightened arousal of the sympathetic nervous system, when chronic, leads to increased serum cholesterol, blood pressure, and cardiac output, all of which can increase the risk of coronary artery disease and heart attack.

In our session together, Roger described how he'd learned to keep his anger under wraps, restraining himself from chewing people out when they didn't do things exactly his way. He got similarly angry at anything that blocked his compulsive need to control things, like having to wait in line. Repressing anger is very dangerous to the body, however, since it results in elevated blood pressure and other damaging cardiovascular changes. Learning to deal with emotions, as we'll do in Chapter 7, was an important part of Roger's mind/body program, as was breaking the cycle of anxiety and impatience by using the two techniques you'll learn in this chapter.

Roger told me frankly that he wanted to lower his blood pressure behaviorally so he could avoid medications, some of which can cause sexual dysfunction in males. Before his visit, he had already begun his own program for physical well-being. He'd taken up jogging for cardiovascular exercise, reduced his salt intake, and lost ten pounds. What needed attention next was his behavior. Roger's inner dialogue revolved around constant self-doubt, to which he responded by trying to control every possible circumstance. Life was one big threat. This was the cause of his performance anxiety. And he was almost phobic about public speaking, which was an important part of his job. Roger would begin to worry about his presentation a week in advance, always awfulizing about its outcome. He fantasized that he'd panic and become tongue-tied during his speech or during the question-and-answer period. He was terrified of not knowing an answer and of not being able to articulate what he wanted to say. His worst fear was being exposed as a fraud and losing his job. Roger carefully explained to me what happened before a speech. His mouth became extremely dry, his palms became sweaty, his heart pounded, and he had a sinking sensation in his stomach. These anxiety cues became part of a feedback loop that made him even more anxious. His hands trembled and his chest muscles tightened, causing him discomfort. He would then start to wonder if he was having a heart attack, escalating the anxiety cycle into high gear.

Once you've begun to awfulize, engaging the fight-or-flight response, you tend to lose perspective. Instead of thinking about all his successful presentations, Roger dwelled on disaster. He would lose control. This time he would be exposed. Once on track, the anxious mind is like a pit bull on a rampage; it's hard to distract. One-track thinking is adaptive in cases where you're actually in an emergency situation and need full attention to escape. In situations that are only mentally threatening, however, this survival wiring can become a trap. The worried mind engages the fight-or-flight circuits. The muscles tense up and heighten anxiety even further. The question for Roger, and any of us who become trapped by anxiety, is how to break this cycle.

Cutting through the Anxiety Cycle

Take a moment to review how anxious, awfulizing thoughts lead both to *visceral feedback* and to *musculoskeletal feedback.* Roger experienced anxiety both ways. Viscerally, he was aware of dry mouth, sweaty palms, and a racing heart, and he also felt a sinking sensation in the pit of his stomach. These were all feedback from his autonomic nervous system. When Roger perceived these symptoms, his mind interpreted them as threats, which, through fight-or-flight, increased his arousal level even more. This vicious cycle can culminate in complete helplessness if it escalates to panic. The attempt to stay in control leads paradoxically to exactly such a loss of control.

Roger's sense of losing control was amplified by the response of his musculoskeletal system to his awfulizing thoughts. Roger's chest was tense, and he could see his hands shaking. These cues also fed back to increase the speed of his thoughts, adding thoughts about whether he could have a heart attack or drop his papers.

Take a moment now and close your eyes. Recall a time (choose one that is not extremely upsetting or traumatic) when you felt anxious, allowing yourself to relive it in as much detail as you're comfortable with. See if you can tell whether you react predominantly with physical tension or with autonomic arousal. Remember, this situation is in the past, and your response to it now is one of those things that really is under your control!

The two following cycle breakers will help you deal with the anxiety cycle.

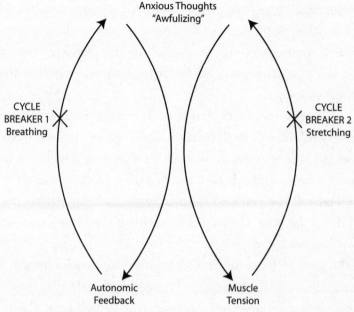

FIGURE 3.1 Cycle Breakers

Cycle Breaker 1: Breathing

An old fable concerns a poor man who, while wandering through the forest one day, discovers a dusty blue bottle. As he brushes it off, out pops a genie! The genie promises to fulfill as many wishes as the man can think of, with one condition: Should the man run out of wishes, the genie can devour him. The poor man agrees, figuring that he can easily occupy the genie. His first wish is for a meal. The genie produces it instantly—row after row of steaming delicacies. As the poor man gazes at all this food, he thinks of servants to feed him. No sooner does this thought reach his consciousness than it's fulfilled. One wish follows another. Soon he's in a beautiful mansion with a charming wife and wonderful children. With difficulty, they keep the genie busy, but soon the man and his wife start to worry that they'll run out of wishes.

The man remembers that a wise man lives in a hermitage about two hours away. He and his wife go to the hermitage in hopes that the wise man will have a solution that will save them from the genie. Indeed, he does. He tells the pair to erect a tall pole and tell the genie to keep busy by endlessly shinnying up and down the pole. If they need anything, they can just call him down for a moment.

The genie, of course, is a metaphor for our own minds. The minute the mind is not actively engaged, it threatens to eat us up with anxieties and negative fantasies. Shinnying up and down the pole is a metaphor for the breathing process. If the mind is kept busy noticing the incoming and outgoing breath, then it has no chance to overcome us. We can call on it as our servant rather than allowing it to eat us up.

Breathing is an autonomic—or essentially automatic—bodily function that proceeds on its own but that we can also change voluntarily. While it's impossible for most of us (unless we are yogis) to decide how fast we'd like our hearts to beat, all of us can change the rhythm and depth of breathing. Changing breathing can, in turn, reduce or increase sympathetic nervous system activity, triggering either the fight-or-flight response or the relaxation response.

Learning to notice your breathing pattern and being able to change it from tension-producing to relaxation-inducing is one of the most crucial—and simplest—mind/body skills. This skill interrupts the genie of the mind, and that interruption is sometimes all that's required to let go of anxiety-producing thoughts. (In other instances, it's important to examine the thoughts themselves—where they come from and how they can be changed or attended to by taking necessary action. We'll explore that dimension in Chapters 5 and 6.)

Abdominal Breathing: Relaxed Mode

If you've ever closely observed a baby breathing, you've had an excellent demonstration of proper technique. When a baby breathes in, you can watch how its abdomen expands like a balloon, and when it breathes out, you can see the abdomen flattening. When we fall asleep at night, exactly the same pattern occurs. In fact, whenever we're truly relaxed, the body reverts to abdominal breathing.

The diaphragm is a large sheet of muscle located just underneath the lungs, separating the lung cavity from the abdominal cavity. In Figure 3.2, you can see that it's shaped like an inverted bowl or dome. It contracts and moves down, flattening out during inhalation. Its downward movement creates a negative pressure in the lungs, and the lower lobes fill with air. Since its downward motion pushes on the organs within the abdominal cavity, the belly expands as the breath comes in. Exhalation is nothing more than a letting down. The diaphragm pops back up into its relaxed position, pushing the air out of the lungs. The belly then flattens back down. The bottom five pairs of ribs are called the floating ribs. They expand through the action of both the

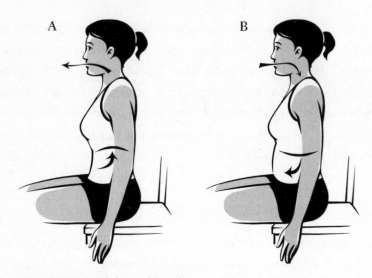

FIGURE 3.2 Abdominal Breathing
A. EXHALE
Diaphragm relaxes, pushing air out.
(Belly in)
B. INHALE
Diaphragm contracts, pulling air in.
(Belly out)

diaphragm and the intercostal (between-ribs) muscles and fill the middle portion of the lungs after the lower lobes are filled by the action of the diaphragm. The last portion of the lungs to fill is the upper portion, ending just below the collarbone. In proper breathing, there is a complete exchange of air in the lower, middle, and upper portions of the lungs.

Unfortunately, once infancy passes and we begin to live in the fantasies of the mind more than the reality of the moment, the breathing pattern begins to shift as well, mirroring our various emotional states. Breathing is truly the mirror of the psyche. Recall for a moment the last time you felt frightened. What happened to your breathing? Chances are that you either held your breath—breathing stopped altogether—or that your breathing became fast, shallow, and erratic.

Remember the autonomic changes that occur with anxiety? Breathing is one of those changes and sets the tone of the rest of the autonomic nervous system. Proper breathing is really a minirelaxation response, creating almost identical physiology. It makes good sense. When the mind is at rest and we're experiencing peacefulness, breathing is relaxed. If the mind is stormy, creating waves that obscure peacefulness (remember that pearl resting at the bottom of a calm pond?), calming your breathing automatically restores peace of mind. This is one feedback cycle that works to our advantage!

Chest Breathing: Tense Mode

The glamorous ideal of puffed-out chest and flat belly, for both men and women, is the antithesis of proper breathing. If you hold your belly in or if you force it in with tight clothing, you effectively freeze the diaphragm, making abdominal breathing impossible. The way to a trim belly is through moderate eating and appropriate exercise, not through holding your breath. In fact, when you learn to breathe properly, using the abdominal muscles, it will actually help to flatten your belly. As long as you hold the belly rigid, breathing can occur only in the upper portion of the chest. The typical chest breath moves only about 500 cubic centimeters of air—about half a pint. A full diaphragmatic or abdominal breath moves eight to ten times that volume!

You can probably appreciate how tiring the extra muscle activity is to breathe fast enough to move all that additional air with only the intercostal muscles. People who complain of fatigue are often amazed at the difference proper breathing can make. It not only eliminates the needless effort of chest breathing but also supplies more oxygen for fuel. The brain is the organ with the greatest oxygen need, and you will notice a difference in your level of alertness immediately after just ten or so proper breaths. When you think about "brain food," the best fuel of all is oxygen, and the best way to deliver it in precisely the right quantity is through abdominal breathing.

Learning to Breathe

STEP 1: How am I breathing?

Since most of us are unaware of breathing, we have no chance to use it to our own advantage. In this exercise you'll learn to identify abdominal and chest breathing so that you can learn to breathe properly.

Sit in a straight-backed chair and then slide forward a few inches so that you're reclining slightly. You can put a pillow behind your lower back if you like.

Place one hand palm down over your navel and place the other hand on top of it.

Without trying to change your breathing in any way, simply notice whether your belly is expanding or flattening as you inhale. It's easiest to do this if you close your eyes so that you can concentrate.

Take a moment and try this now, noticing the next five breaths. If your belly expands as you breathe in, you're breathing at least in part from your diaphragm. If your belly doesn't move or goes flat as you inhale, you're breathing from your chest.

STEP 2: Shifting from chest to abdominal breathing

Take a deep breath in and then blow it out completely through your mouth, like an audible sigh of relief. As you do this, notice how your belly flattens, and flatten it even further, squeezing out every last bit of air. Now just let the next breath flow in by itself through your nose. Can you feel your belly expand? If not, try again, or try the visualization that you learned in the last chapter. Imagine a balloon filling in your belly on the in breath and emptying on the out breath. Or perhaps you can imagine your belly expanding and relaxing in some other way that feels more authentic and familiar to you.

The trick to shifting from chest to diaphragmatic breathing is to exhale completely for just one breath. This is why we exhale the one breath through the mouth—to fully evacuate the lungs. This full exhalation pushes out all the stale air from the bottom of the lungs, and the resulting vacuum automatically pulls in a deep, diaphragmatic breath. *You need to breathe out deeply only once or twice. Think of it as a sigh of relief.* Sighing and yawning both result in a deep air exchange and are the body's way of letting go of stress and tension.

Continue breathing through your nose, imagining that the incoming breath is filling a balloon in your belly or whatever image works best for you. When your belly is full, let go and feel the balloon emptying as you exhale. Two or three minutes of abdominal breathing provide a time-out from tension. Even two or three breaths make a difference.

Practicing Abdominal Breathing

Whenever you get caught up in anxiety—worry and tension—you can break the cycle by shifting into abdominal breathing. Once you've mastered it by practicing with eyes closed—which may take up to several weeks—you can do it while keeping your eyes open. Then you'll find that it works anywhere and at any time. Standing in your kitchen, waiting in line, riding in an elevator, driving down the highway, you can always breathe.

Several years ago I was at a scientific meeting with a friend where biofeedback equipment was being sold. As a sales come-on, one manufacturer was using a biofeedback machine that monitored finger temperature to create a diabolical game: Who could relax the fastest? What happens when you play a game and win a point? You become excited, right? That turns on your autonomic nervous system, you get tense, and then your hands get cold. The more relaxed, the warmer your hands and feet. My friend and I decided to give it a try. At first we were running at a dead heat. We'd each win a point, get excited, cool down, and lose the next. Then I remembered to breathe. I forgot about the game, exhaled a slow sigh of relief, shifted to abdominal breathing, and just concentrated on the rise and fall of my belly for the next minute. By the end of that time I'd won the game.

Remember, take a deep breath and let it go with a relaxing, contented sigh of relief. Then feel the next several breaths entering the belly, letting it expand on the in breath, letting go on the out breath.

The Ten-to-One Countdown

One simple breathing technique combines abdominal (belly) breathing with meditation to produce a deep, quick change in physiology and attitude. Breathe in and let go with a sigh to shift to abdominal breathing. Take another breath, and in your mind's eye watch it fill your belly. As you breathe out, silently repeat *ten,* letting go of tension as if it were a wave moving from your head, down your body, and out through the soles of your feet. Imagine the feeling of letting go. On the next breath, repeat the technique, counting *nine* on the out breath. On the eight subsequent breaths count back all the way down to *one.* Unlike in Dr. Benson's experiment, where students lost count, here you're only counting down once and in one direction. If you do lose count, don't worry. Pick up wherever you think you are. *Take a moment and try this now before reading on.*

Notice how you're feeling? More relaxed, right? You may also notice that your breathing has slowed way down—a sign of the relaxation response. As you become more proficient with this technique through practice, you require shorter and shorter sessions because your nervous system has learned another beneficial conditioned response. Just two or three breaths will bring you many of the benefits of a longer period of meditation.

Cycle Breaker 2: Stretching

After a few weeks of practice, Roger was able to use breathing to relax at home and work. Ten minutes before a talk, he'd close his office door and do five minutes of belly breathing. As he walked to a conference room, he would breathe. As he got his slides in order, he would breathe. After about a month, Roger reported that meditation and breathing had reduced his performance anxiety to a manageable level. Although his blood pressure also came down, he continued to feel fidgety and had difficulty sitting quietly. In anxiety-provoking situations, his breathing calmed his autonomic symptoms, but his chest and shoulders were still very tight. To relax those muscles, Roger had to learn to deescalate the anxiety feedback loop bodily.

In this next session I'm going to lead you through two brief body relaxations. The first is the Anytime Series. It takes just two to three minutes to complete and can be done in a chair at home, in the office, on the bus, or anyplace at all. The second is the Full-Body Relaxer Series, which requires fifteen to twenty minutes and a place large enough to stretch out on a rug or mat on the floor.

The Anytime Series

This series is composed of four exercises followed by the ten-to-one countdown. It's designed to relax tension as quickly and efficiently as possible in some of the major areas where people store tension: back, chest, shoulders, neck, and face.

All the exercises are based on the same principle. Various body parts are *tensed on the in breath* and *relaxed on the out breath.* Every out breath is an opportunity to let go—cooperating with gravity. Before beginning, take a moment to notice your breathing. If it's in your chest, breathe a sigh of relief and watch your belly expand like a balloon on the next in breath. Now notice your torso. Your whole upper body rises up on the in breath and sinks back down on the out breath, letting go to the pull of gravity, which is a natural ally. A lot of useless tension gets created by opposing the pull of gravity and contracting muscles that aren't even being used.

The best way to learn these exercises is to read through the following paragraph and practice what you'll be doing in a general way. Next, look at the illustrations and imagine how each exercise will feel. You can also follow along on the CD *Meditations for Relaxation and Stress Reduction*, or on the video *Inner Peace for Busy People*, where these exercises are included as bonus material. Ordering information for these products is included in the resource section at the end of the book.

For now, sit comfortably in your chair with both feet on the floor and your arms resting lightly on your thighs (try putting the book in a holder on a table in front of you while you follow along—or have some one else read the remainder of the paragraph to you, or record the exercise and play it back for yourself). As you're reading—*right now*—breathe out a sigh of relief, switch to abdominal breathing, and then breathe back from three to one, concentrating on the way that your body relaxes a little more as you let go from head to foot. Now, notice your jaw muscles. Are your teeth clenched, which tightens the jaw, or is the lower part of your face relaxed? Let your teeth relax, your mouth open slightly, and your jaws soften and relax a little more on each out breath. Now, notice your eyes. Let them soften as you breathe. Now your shoulders. Are they tensed up? Perhaps there's room for them to drop further down, a little bit more on each out breath. Let your arms and hands relax more, feeling heavier and heavier as they rest on your legs. Take a deep breath and let your chest muscles relax. Finally, feel your relaxed belly expanding and letting go again with each breath.

The four Anytime Exercises that follow will allow you to let go of even more tension. *Make a note of where you feel residual tension right now* so that you can check your level of relaxation at the end.

Exercise 1: The back relaxer

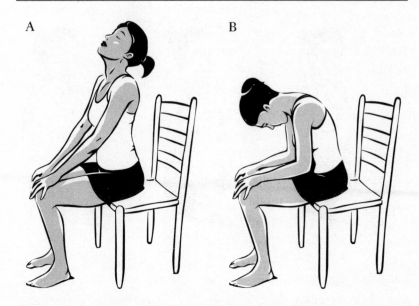

Move to the edge of your chair. With eyes closed so that you can pay closer attention to your inner sensations, notice how your back feels. On the next in breath, arch gently backward (A), stretching your spine only as far as feels comfortable. Exhale and round your back (B), rolling your shoulders forward and letting your head fall gently forward. Repeat three times, keeping full attention on breathing, stretching, and letting go.

Exercise 2: Shoulder shrugs

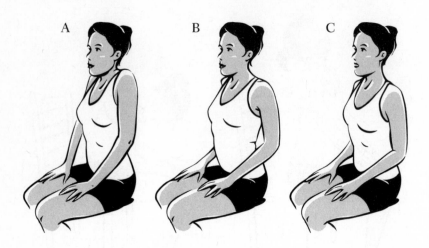

Inhale and pull your shoulders up to your ears (A). Now rotate your shoulders backward, pulling the shoulder blades together (B). Exhale with a sigh and let go (C). Repeat three times. Notice that when you pull your shoulder blades together, you are giving the chest muscles a nice, relaxing stretch. Repeat the exercise, rotating your shoulders forward three times.

Exercise 3: Neck relaxer

Exhale and drop your head gently toward your right shoulder, taking care
to relax your left shoulder so that it doesn't rise up. Don't worry if your
head hardly moves at all at first. Just feel the gentle stretch on the left
side of your neck, letting your head drop further toward your shoulder
naturally for three out breaths. Let gravity do the work and don't strain
at all! Bring your head back up.

Exhale and drop your head very slowly toward your left shoulder, taking
care to relax your right shoulder so that it doesn't rise up. Feel the gentle stretch on the right side of your neck, letting your head drop further
toward your shoulder naturally for three out breaths. Remember to be
gentle with yourself, surrendering to gravity rather than straining. Bring
your head back up.

Exhale as you bring your chin toward your chest. Take three breaths, relaxing a little bit more on each out breath as you feel the back of your
neck gently stretching and your face becoming softer and more relaxed.
Bring your head back up.

Exhale and drop your head toward your back, letting your mouth fall
open. You'll feel a gentle stretch to your throat as the back of your neck
softens and relaxes. Continue for three breaths and then bring your
head back up.

Exercise 4: Face exercises

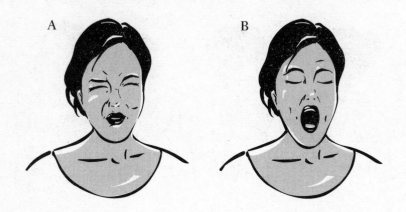

A   B

The facial exercises are done in two steps. First, inhale and scrunch all your facial muscles in toward the center (A). It's as if you're trying to squeeze all the tension right off the tip of your nose. Exhale and let it go. SMILE and take a few normal breaths. Now inhale and open your mouth wide, lifting your eyebrows to make your face very long (B). This is like a yawn. When you exhale and let go, you may even find yourself yawning. SMILE!

The Full-Body Relaxer Series

The following seven stretches were chosen to relax the major muscle groups. In doing these exercises, keep two things in mind.

1. These are gentle letting-go stretches. The best way to develop a supple, limber, and relaxed body is to focus on *melting* into each stretch. *Never bounce or push beyond what feels comfortable.* Bouncing defeats the purpose of stretching because the quick pull on the muscle fibers alerts special sensors within the muscle to the sudden overstretch. Nerve signals from those receptors then automatically shorten the muscle. Bouncing therefore causes muscle fibers to shorten and tense rather than lengthen and relax. Bouncing can also strain or tear muscles as you pull on a group of shortened muscle fibers.

2. If you have any physical problem that limits your ability to exercise, consult with your physician before doing these or any other exercises. Taking responsibility for knowing your own limits is an important mind/body skill in itself, since many stressed people got that way in the first place through a tendency to overdo things! Read each exercise through and study the illustration *before* you try it.

Relaxer 1: The wall hang

Note: If you have any tendency toward back pain, bend your knees slightly before you begin to avoid any strain on your lower back.

Stand with your back to the wall, feet about shoulder width apart and nine to twelve inches out from the wall. Press the small of your back against the wall so that every vertebra is in contact with it. Close your eyes, breathe out a sigh of relief, and shift to abdominal breathing. Breathe slowly and naturally throughout this exercise. Begin by dropping your chin toward your chest. Drop your shoulders forward and then begin peeling your backbone off the wall, a single vertebra at a time if you can, continuing to drop forward. Your hips will slide up the wall as your upper body drops down. When you have dropped as far as you can, just hang there. Let your head and shoulders go like a rag doll. Take several breaths as you hang loose. Now gradually come back up, thinking about reattaching your vertebrae to the wall, one at a time. When you get back up, lean against the wall, breathing abdominally, to rest.

Relaxer 2: The fountain

Stand with your legs about a shoulder width apart. Inhale and stretch your arms *way up* over your head, locking your thumbs together, feeling the stretch along your sides and making your spine long. Exhale, circling to the left. Inhale and stretch way up again, exhale, and circle left. Go once more to the left and then reverse, three times to the right. Remember to just let go without pushing or straining. The idea is to be curious about what you feel, enjoying the sensations, rather than trying to touch the floor and move further into the pose. *Again, if you have any tendency toward back pain, bend your knees a little.*

Relaxer 3: The cat

A

B

Get down on all fours. Inhale, lifting your head up and pushing your spine down, feeling it lengthen as your head reaches up (A). Let your belly balloon out. Exhale, dropping your head and arching your back up like an angry cat, pulling in your abdominal muscles (B). Repeat three to five times.

Relaxer 4: Leg extensions

Still on all fours, inhale as you lift your head up and extend your right leg out behind you (A), toes pointed. Exhale, dropping your head down and bending your leg inward as you bring your knee toward your forehead (B). Repeat three times on the right side and three times on the left.

Relaxer 5: Forward bends

In this three-part exercise, you lengthen your torso and stretch out first over the right leg, then the left, and finally both. Start by sitting up straight with both legs stretched out straight in front of you. Make sure you're sitting on your sit bones rather than your padding! Bend your left leg, placing the heel next to your groin, as if you were going to sit cross-legged. Inhale, stretching your arms high above your head. Turn slightly to your left, facing your toes, exhale, and stretch forward *from the hips* (rather than rounding your back) over the outstretched leg. Hold onto your leg wherever it is comfortable to do so—whether at the knee, the shin, the ankle, or the foot if you're very limber. On each of the next five exhales, see if you can lift your torso, *move from your hips*, and come a little further into the stretch. Most of the power that helps you bend forward comes from your abdominal muscles. Repeat on the left side for five breaths. Now stretch both legs out in front of you, next to one another, and repeat the stretch a last time, lengthening yourself out and coming down over both legs together. Move into the stretch for five breaths.

Relaxer 6: Pelvic tilt

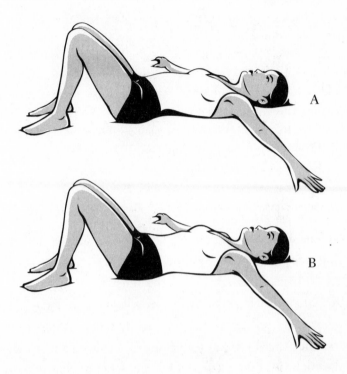

Lie down on your back and bring your knees up so that your feet are on the floor, close to your buttocks. Flatten your back against the floor by tilting your pelvis backward. Tilt your pelvis forward and let the space between the small of your back and the floor reappear. Now coordinate the movements with your breathing. Inhale as you rock the pelvis forward, making the space (A). Let your belly fill as you do this. Exhale as you rock backward, flattening your back against the floor (B). With a little practice, you'll get the idea of pressing your vertebrae onto the floor one at a time and picking them up off the floor in the same fashion. This is an excellent exercise for back tension. Repeat ten to twelve times or until you feel a release.

Relaxer 7: Final relaxation

Lie on your back with your legs on the floor, placed comfortably apart so that your toes point out gently toward either side. (If you have back pain, you'll be more comfortable putting a pillow under your knees: Let your body be your guide.) Let your arms rest a foot or so away from your body, and rotate your shoulder blades together (like tucking imaginary wings against your back) so that your palms turn up. Take five abdominal breaths, letting go a little more on each out breath and letting yourself sink down into your mat.

Progressive Muscle Relaxation

1. Inhale and lift your right leg about a foot off the floor, making a fist with your toes and tensing leg and foot as much as feels good for you. Hold the tension for a few seconds and then exhale very slowly as you lower your leg, unclench your foot, and let all the tension flow out. When your leg reaches the floor, roll your foot from side to side to aid relaxation. Be curious, and savor the feelings that remain for this and all the other exercises in this series.

2. Repeat on the left side.

3. Inhale and tense your buttocks, making them as hard as rocks (buns of steel!). Hold the tension for a few seconds, then exhale and let go.

4. Inhale and puff out your belly as far as it will go. Hold for a few seconds, then exhale and let it flatten.

5. Inhale and puff out your chest as far as you can. Hold for a few seconds and then exhale and let go.

6. Inhale, and lift your right arm off the mat, make a fist, and tense the arm. Hold for a few seconds then exhale and let your arm relax back into the mat.
7. Inhale and lift your left arm off the mat, make a fist, and tense the arm. Hold for a few seconds, then exhale and let go.
8. Roll your head from side to side several times, breathing abdominally.
9. Inhale, scrunching your face toward the middle, then exhale and let go.
10. Inhale, making a yawning face with open mouth and raised eyebrows, then exhale and let go.

Be careful not to overdo the tension. The idea is to cultivate the sense of what tension and relaxation feel like, rather than to crunch your body into a caricature of Popeye the Sailor Man flexing his biceps.

The Complete Breath

The perfect end to a period of relaxation is the complete breath. It's a variant of the abdominal breathing that you're already familiar with. Imagine that in place of your lungs there is a pear-shaped balloon with a long neck. The round part of the balloon is located in your belly, and the long neck extends up through the middle and upper chest. When you breathe in, imagine the belly expanding as the round part of the balloon fills. Then feel the neck of the balloon starting to fill as your middle chest expands.

Finally, feel the top of the balloon filling up under the collarbone. As you exhale, feel the top of the balloon under the collarbone empty first, then feel the middle of the balloon emptying as your chest begins to flatten, and finally feel the round part of the balloon flatten as your belly shrinks back down toward the floor.

Take ten complete breaths, concentrating on feeling how the air fills the abdomen, the middle chest, and finally the top of the chest, and then noticing how it leaves the top of the chest, the middle, and finally the abdomen. This breath is particularly restful. It can be used not only at the end of a relaxation period but, like abdominal breathing, anytime you need to break the anxiety cycle.

Breathing and Pain

Pain can be broken down into two parts. The first layer is the physical reality of the pain itself. The second added layer is the attitude you have about the pain. My migraines are an example. Although they are much milder and less frequent now that I know more about minding the body and mending the mind, they used to be excruciating. The pain was intense—throbbing pain that turned me nauseous at its crescendos—stabbing pain that made light intolerable. The second layer of the pain was the attitude that I added—the uncertainty about when the pain would pass, the impatience at being dragged out of my life and dropped into bed, the anger at my body's betrayal, the self-blame for being sickly, the helplessness and panic at being out of control, and the final layer of blame for letting things get so far out of hand. My body's response to that second layer was to get tense. Very tense. All my facial muscles tensed up around the headache and made the physical pain worse. In addition to the headache pain, the anxiety worsened the nausea and vomiting. This cycle of pain-anxiety-pain escalates endlessly, making pain worse and worse.

The actual sensory experience of pain has a lot to do with attitude. A child who cut his leg while picking out his birthday present at the toy store would experience much less pain than the child who cut himself in math class. If a pain equivalent to childbirth were experienced from an automobile accident, the additional fear of the circumstance would render it much more intense. A friend of mine who is a gynecologist often explains it this way to her patients who suffer from premenstrual syndrome: "If you have a broken arm and life is going along fine, you hardly notice it. But if the boss is yelling and you're having a fight with your husband, the pain is a lot more disabling."

The most harmful attitude toward pain is to tense up around it physically or mentally, trying to push it away. All that resistance accomplishes is to increase the physical pain and the second, or added, layer of attitudinal discomfort. The premise we speak of again and again is that *whatever you resist persists.* The harder you try to escape, the more stuck you become. The big "reframe" in looking at pain is to accept it, relaxing around it physically and mentally. This means that you shift into the position of being an accepting observer of your pain rather than an unwilling victim. It doesn't require much thought to see that the observer has much more control than the victim. *To be in control of pain, you have to let go of trying to push it away.*

The next question is: What keeps you holding on? Sometimes it's lack of awareness. If you don't know that you've been holding on, then you can't let go. It's just like the ability to release tension in your shoulders as soon as you've taken a moment to observe that they're tense in the first place. Awareness of yourself, physically and mentally, is the first step.

A common reason for not wanting to let go of pain is that there's something that you need from it and think you can't get any other way. Consider my migraines. I'd overcommit to the point where I knew it was impossible to get everything done, and then I'd get increasingly tense and anxious. Then I'd complain and blame other people for putting me in a situation that I'd obviously created myself. The stress and strain would escalate, and sooner or later a headache would begin.

The headache served several useful purposes. First, it showed those "insensitive" others whom I was blaming for my own overcommitment how mean they were and how much they hurt me. Second, it was the only legitimate way to get any rest and not have to produce for a while. A migraine headache takes precedence over anything that may need to be done. Third, it was the only way my body knew to release all the tension it had stored up. A migraine always felt like a storm to me. When it was over, I lay limp, washed clean, and totally relaxed. Too bad that my body had to fight itself practically to death and then lie exhausted in order to let go.

Many of us do the same thing with pain and other illnesses and anxieties. Psychologists call these benefits of illness secondary gain. Why would I want to let go of the migraines? I needed them. As big as the price was in the economy of my body/mind, clearly the migraines were worthwhile. The body/mind has incredible wisdom. It will seek whatever way it can, at the least possible cost, to bring us into a state of balance and self-regulation.

But don't go overboard here! Sometimes there are no secondary gains to an illness—it just is what it is. But the simple exercise of inquiring honestly into your own experience—and identifying any secondary gains that *might* be operating—can produce great insight. If you, like me, do find secondary gains, then the challenge—a truly fascinating one—is to find healthy ways to get the same needs met. In the case of my migraines, doing everything myself just had to stop. And believe me, learning to ask for help was a graduate program in humility, honesty, and balance.

Using the Breath to Let Go of Pain

I've used the kind of meditation and yoga breathing that you're already familiar with to cope with migraines since the late 1960s. But I first learned about applying mindfulness to pain reduction from my colleague Dr. Jon Kabat-Zinn. His landmark book, *Full Catastrophe Living: Using the Wisdom of Your Body and Mind to Face Stress, Pain, and Illness,* gives an excellent description of how mindfulness—moment-to-moment awareness without judgment or preference—invites pain relief. Mindfulness training was first introduced into behavioral medicine in the late 1970s by Dr. Kabat-Zinn at the stress reduction and relaxation clinic that he founded and directed at the University of Massachusetts Medical School. He had noted that this central component of Buddhist meditation practice was described traditionally as leading to the relief of pain and suffering. In a study of 225 chronic pain patients trained in mindfulness meditation techniques, which included stretching and breathing, he found that most patients continued to practice one or more of the techniques, and particularly the mindful breathing, for up to four years following their training. The large majority reported lasting moderate to great improvement in their pain over this time period. Some of the suggestions you're about to read for practicing mindfulness for pain relief are derived from Dr. Kabat-Zinn's work.

Here's the basic idea—modified through my own personal and clinical experience—and blended with the use of imagination. Close your eyes and shift your attention inward to abdominal breathing. As you continue to breathe, let yourself become more and more aware of the pain (the immediate physical sensations rather than your thoughts about it). This is effective not only for physical pain, but for emotional pain such as anxiety, guilt, fear, sadness, or depression that settles in your heart, belly, throat, or muscles. *Don't close off.* Open up to the physical dimensions of the pain and be curious about it. Be present to its nuances. At first, as you dare to begin noticing it, it may seem more intense. Then it may flicker off and on or change positions. A pain can transform into heat or an electrical feeling, or it can transform into pleasure since the two sensations are actually close from a neuroanatomical perspective. Keep breathing abdominally and "watching" the pain, observing it with all your inner senses. That's the mindfulness aspect, and for many people it works wonders. Pain that was intense going into a meditation may change dramatically, just by being present with it, instead of resisting it.

I like to add another component to working with pain. Once you've become mindful and present to the pain, imagine that you can breathe in and out of it just as you can imagine breathing in and out of your belly. Imagine the breath as loving attention—the opposite of trying to push something away. It helps to support your imagination by recalling a loving memory. I often go back to one of nursing my youngest son, rocking in a chair, and cuddling the totally relaxed, content baby. You can feel your body's response to remembered love; it's an expansive, open, receptive kind of feeling. As you breathe in, let such a feeling surround and penetrate the pain. Cradle it as you would a child or a beloved pet. *Does the pain have a color or a shape?* Imagine the love breaking it up and dissolving it like an Alka Seltzer tablet dropped into a glass of water. Breathe out the residue.

Perhaps the pain will break up during the meditation. Perhaps you'll feel it ease up later. But if you try this visualization and then immediately begin to judge the results, you'll soon be caught by the pain again. Adopting an attitude of allowing—of curiosity and receptivity rather than judgment and preference—lets you engage the pain in a new way. This kind of engagement, you might recall, is the quality of *commitment,* one of the three attitudes of stress hardiness. It's more than an approach to pain. It's an enlightened attitude that can transform your entire life.

SUGGESTIONS FOR THE READER

1. Observe how you react to anxiety-provoking situations this week. Are you primarily an autonomic reactor or a muscular-tension reactor? Make note of this. Perhaps you respond in different ways to different hassles.

2. Practice abdominal breathing several times daily. Put up little signs where you'll see them as reminders.

3. Practice the Anytime Series whenever and wherever you feel tension. *The time to do it is when you feel as if you don't*

have the time, perhaps when you're tense and rushed. It takes only a few minutes but will save you many more by allowing you to carry on in a more relaxed, centered way. This series is great preventive medicine. Letting go of tension before your muscles set like concrete is infinitely better than ending up with a headache, muscle spasm, or tension that requires massage or muscle relaxants to let go of.

4. Practice the Full-Body Relaxer Series daily if you can, and you'll see remarkable changes both in your awareness and in your flexibility. You can then use the whole series or any part when you need it, although practicing several times a week is the most beneficial. The progressive muscle relaxation and complete breathing can be used anytime and is great in bed if you're having trouble falling asleep.

5. The complete breath can be used alone anytime. Although it's easier to do initially while lying down, with experience you'll soon be able to do it sitting up.

6. For most people, the best way to learn effective stretching coupled with breathing is to look for a community class in hatha yoga. Yoga classes vary. Some are oriented entirely toward the physical, and others may incorporate a mind/body approach or a spiritual component. Be sure to choose the kind of class that suits you.

7. If you're working with a pain problem, consider whether there might be any secondary gains. Write them down and consider healthier ways of getting your needs met.

CHAPTER 4

Mindfulness and the Discovery of the Self

Anyone who has ever sat at home healthy, well fed, surrounded by loved ones, and suffering from intense anxiety will readily agree that peace of mind is the necessary condition for happiness. But how can we possibly learn to have peace of mind when the mind is by nature restless, projecting its wants and fears endlessly into the past and the future?

Think about your favorite activity for a moment. When you're really enjoying something you like, how do you feel? As you listen to your favorite music with full attention, other thoughts and desires fade away. You're simply in the moment. There's contentment—peace. Inevitably, of course, your mind kicks back in. How can you sit and listen to music? You need to clean the house, or think about your job, or get something to eat, or worry about finances, or make a phone call, or any of a thousand things. No longer in the moment, you're off and running.

If you could train your mind to let go of other desires, returning to them when the actual moment has come to do the bills and make the phone call, you'd be able to experience peace of mind. One road to peace is through a practice called mindfulness that Dr. Jon Kabat-Zinn, whom you met in the last chapter, introduced to the field of stress management and mind/body medicine. His excellent book, *Wherever You Go, There You Are*, is a practical adventure in living an awakened, mindful life.

Alice, a brave and courageous woman, was a poet and fiction writer in her midforties when I met her in the early 1980s. An inspiring example of the power of mindful awareness, she was a member of the very first Mind/Body Group and a great teacher to me. Suffering from severe allergies, she could be laid up with debilitating dizziness by such seemingly innocuous events as a whiff of perfume or an unexpected ingredient in a meal. Alice found that several long periods of meditation during the day helped her allergies. She became a serious student of mindfulness meditation. This meditative practice consists of anchoring attention in the breath and then passively observing thoughts, feelings, perceptions, and sensations without judgment. Ideas of good and bad fade away as a contented openness to the present moment emerges.

After becoming a committed meditator, Alice was in a near-fatal car crash. Her chest was crushed and her brain damaged when the car her husband was driving spun out of control on an icy road. Alice was given a 1 percent chance to live. Her recovery process was truly remarkable. After several weeks in the intensive care unit, Alice was moved to a rehabilitation hospital. Her entire vocabulary consisted of a few hundred words. Like some stroke

patients, she had lost access to language. I can hardly begin to imagine the frustration for anyone, let alone for such a wonderful writer. Alice had also lost the ability to control her body. She was like a toddler who had to relearn the most basic skills of language and locomotion.

Alice smiled at me as she recalled the process of relearning how to walk. Each step was a meditation. Her entire concentration had to be riveted on the minutest sensations of walking; otherwise she would fall. When talking, she had to give full attention to stringing the words into a sentence. When playing with blocks to recover spatial skills, she had to perform every motion with complete awareness, with full attention. Every digression into mindlessness was obvious, since she could no longer perform the task. Normally, we have little awareness of where the mind is. Alice viewed this quick "feedback" system as a gift. Her disabilities became powerful teachers of how to live in the moment.

Mindfulness: Meditation in Action

Mindfulness is meditation in action and involves a "be here now" approach that allows life to unfold without the limitation of prejudgment. It means being open to an awareness of the moment as it is and to what is freshly emergent. This form of perception is very different from our normal way of seeing the world, in which we more often see our judgments and beliefs about things, rather than the essence of what is truly real. This is like eating the menu and mistaking it for the meal. Mindfulness is a relaxed state of attentiveness to both the inner world of thoughts and feelings and the outer world of perceptions and actions.

Mindfulness means being present with your food when eating, enjoying it rather than thinking about other things. Mindfulness means openness to the experience of motion when taking a walk, and to the sights, sounds, and smells around you. During some of the retreats that I facilitate, participants are invited to take a silent, mindful walk. There's no "purpose" to the walk—nowhere to go and nothing to accomplish. The "goal" is just being present in the process of walking. Most people are amazed at how incredible the commonplace is as the subtlety of nature reveals its treasures. They hear sounds and see sights with new ears and eyes, with the kind of enjoyment a child experiences.

Watch small children at play to see mindfulness in action. They may be playing with a simple object like a bowl. To an adult, the bowl is a container and it belongs in such-and-such a cabinet. To a child, the bowl has no limits. Turned upside down, it's a drum. Turned on its side, it's a wheel. In fantasy it can become a cradle or a bucket or a spaceship to the moon. To a child, everything is fresh and new. The more we think we know it all, the more closed off from the changing experience of life we become.

Mindfulness requires a change in attitude. The joy is not in finishing an activity—the joy is in doing it. Those of you who are stress junkies will find that this may be completely foreign to your usual modus operandi. Multitasking not only leads to slower reaction times and poor results, but it also favors mindlessness. In reality, we can only do one thing at a time. Although the mind can dart back and forth between several things, it can hold only one thing in full focus. Multitasking, then, actually wastes time both in the back and forth, and in lowered efficiency. In the case of talking on a cell phone while driving, the lost second that researchers have documented in reaction time is enough to cost you—or someone else—a life. And when you interrupt working on a project to check your e-mail, it can take ten or fifteen minutes to get back into the groove of what you were doing. Some of the problems caused by multitasking are summed up delightfully in this story told by psychologist and spiritual teacher Nossrat Peseschkian:

> While on a trip, Abdu'l-Bahá, the son of Bahá u' lláh, the founder of the Bahá'i religion, had been invited to dinner with a family. The wife had good intentions and wanted to show her great culinary artistry. When she brought out the food, she apologized for the fact that it was burned. While cooking it, she had been reading prayers in the hope that the meal would be especially successful. Abdu'l-Bahá answered with a friendly smile and said, "It's good that you pray. But next time you're in the kitchen, pray from a cookbook."

Mindful cooking would have been a truer act of devotion than fragmenting the activities of cooking and praying so that neither one was well accomplished. Vietnamese Buddhist meditation teacher Thich Nhat Hanh, in his book *The Miracle of Mindfulness,* talks about ordinary activities as opportunities to be mindful. Instead of doing the dishes in a hurry, trying to get on to something you'd like better, what if you gave the dishes your full attention? The warmth of the water, the feeling of the soap, the lifting of plates into the dishwater, noticing how your muscles work. These are all pleasant experiences if you're willing to be present to them, instead of to the idea that doing dishes is a chore. Jon Kabat-Zinn successfully adopted the exercise of mindfulness in daily life as part of his stress reduction program, and we in turn, adopted it from him as part of our clinical programs. Twenty-five years later, my own life has been transformed by it.

An Exercise in Mindfulness

STEP 1: Daily Mindfulness Exercise

Choose an activity—brushing your teeth, toweling off after a shower, eating a piece of fruit, making love, literally any activity at all—and do it like a meditation. Mindfully. Try it. You will be amazed at how different a plum—or a kiss—tastes when you're present to the experience.

STEP 2: Opening to the Moment

You can train yourself to be mindful by cultivating aware-ness of where your mind is and then making a choice about where you want it to be. For example, if you need the time walking to the bus stop to plan the day, then you've made a conscious choice. Try to plan without falling into rumina-tion that leads to nothing but tension.

If you don't need to plan, then *just be*. Center on your breathing, let out a sigh of relief, and then let yourself ex-perience the rhythm of breathing and walking. After a while you'll fall into a comfortable stride, perhaps two steps to the in breath and two steps to the out breath, or any cadence that suits you. This can be the focus, the an-chor, that holds your mind still as you open up your atten-tion to what's around you—the trees, the clouds, the people—without judging. Just enjoy the moment.

STEP 3: Awareness of Thought and Physical Reaction

Inevitably, while practicing mindfulness, your mind will wander. Learning to observe where it wanders to is also a practice in awareness. In the last chapter, we began training mindfulness at the most basic levels: the muscles and the autonomic nervous system. Here we become observant of the thoughts that produce these bodily changes. Thoughts are of two varieties:

- Nonafflicting: Thoughts like "I wonder what's for dinner" or "Should I watch TV or read a book?" come and go all the time without getting a rise out of the body. They don't matter that much.

- Afflicting: Thoughts like "I wonder why my spouse and I don't get along" or "I'm scared that my disease is going to kill me" get a definite rise out of the body. They produce an emotional response like fear, guilt, or anger. Because such thoughts draw us out of the present moment, as well as get translated in the body at the emotional level, they're very powerful.

One of my patients, a young nurse who experienced anxiety attacks, was amazed when she realized that the anxiety didn't spring full-blown from nowhere. There were certain thoughts that always preceded her attacks and others that kept them going. When she learned to control her thoughts, her anxiety gradually lessened and then nearly disappeared. As you'll see in the next chapters, it is possible to break the cycle of mindlessness, worry, and past conditioning at many places—thoughts, feelings, or action itself. Let's begin by considering how the mind acquires the conditioned habits that give rise to mindless repetition.

Mental Conditioning

Human learning is a process of conditioning. Once a certain event has occurred, mental impressions are formed that favor its recurrence under similar circumstances. Remember Pavlov's dogs? Actual neural pathways form in response to our experience, much like streambeds that accommodate melting mountain snows. These pathways are familiar grooves, the path of least resistance, and as thoughts travel through them they get deeper and more accommodating. In other words, we all develop thought ruts. Emotional events are conditioned in a similar fashion. Like old programs, stored impressions can start up and run endlessly throughout life. This mindless repetition continues unless we shine the light of awareness on them and change our past conditioning—delete the old programs and lay down new neural tracks—through a process that neuroscientists call neuronal plasticity.

When I was a little girl, I was out walking with my father and a huge black dog came around the corner. My father panicked and immediately pulled me across the street. I was amazed at his fear, since the dog seemed so nice and I'd wanted to pet him. The reality of the animal had very little bearing on our quite different reactions—on the thoughts produced by our minds.

My father's mother had been bitten by a dog when he was a child, and he had a powerful stored impression—a memory—that dogs are frightening and dangerous. I, on the other hand, had been around a wonderfully friendly collie that belonged to my good friend Nancy. My fondest wish was for a dog like hers. We rarely see things for what they are. Instead, we see the reflection of our own past conditioning. We believe and act on opinions and assumptions as if they were reality, shutting out new possibilities. My father was prejudiced against dogs, and this attitude imprisoned him in an apartment for years, since he feared buying a house where there might be big dogs in the neighborhood.

Old programs create walls of many types. Some, like the fear of dogs, are obvious. Others are more subtle. Sometimes, just the conscious awareness of an old pattern is enough to change the situation. Other times, it's just a start.

Ben was a fifty-eight-year-old plumber who came to me with chest pains and insomnia. Almost as an aside, he told me that he had a driving phobia. He could drive during the day, but not at night. He could drive east on the Massachusetts Turnpike, but not west. His phobia had begun about five years earlier, after he recuperated from head injuries that had left him with no memory of how they had occurred.

The usual treatment for a phobia is to enter a relaxed state and then imagine progressively more fear-producing renditions of the phobia while maintaining the state of relaxation. When you can remain relaxed while the mind reruns the fearful fantasy, the conditioned response that leads to the anxiety cycle is broken. The fight-or-flight response is uncoupled from the mind's fantasies. I taught Ben how to meditate and use breathing and stretching to break the anxiety cycle. But his phobia was so powerful, as in cases of posttraumatic stress disorder, that he needed deeper, more specific mind/body work. We decided to try a technique called progressive desensitization, gradually rewiring his fears to a state of relaxation.

Together we constructed a hierarchy, or graded series, of situations that he found threatening. The least threatening was driving in the late afternoon. The most threatening was driving in the dark, west on the turnpike. Ben easily slipped into a meditative state and went through the first rungs of the hierarchy with no problem. Although his mind reran danger, he could allow his body to relax. I was thinking how easy this would be for him. He could replay the tape of our session a few times and then start by driving with his wife at night until in a few weeks he'd be able to drive west on the turnpike alone. We were just approaching that step of the hierarchy when my fantasizing over how easy this would be evaporated.

Ben began to shriek. I put my hand on his shoulder, telling him that he could breathe and let go or breathe and complete whatever was happening inside. After a minute or two, Ben slowly opened his eyes. He shook his head, almost in disbelief: "That was an amazing experience. I can hardly believe it. It was as real as if it were actually happening."

Ben explained the memory that had made him shriek. One evening before Christmas about five years before, he got into his car and headed west on the turnpike. Suddenly he felt a gun barrel on the back of his neck. There were two men in the backseat. They ordered him to pull over to an exit and drive to a big field, where they pistol-whipped and robbed him. Ben woke up in the hospital with a severe concussion and no memory of what had happened.

In the relaxed state of meditation, in which the unconscious mind became accessible, the memory of the forgotten incident had returned. For Ben, understanding the root of the phobia was a breakthrough. He could deal with the reality of what had caused it much better than with its shadow—the pervasive anxiety and chest pain that had left him sleepless for no apparent reason. His chest pain disappeared almost immediately, as did the insomnia, and over the next few months he regained his ability to drive as before, using breathing as a tool to let go and stay relaxed, countering his conditioned fear.

The fears that create conditioned responses like Ben's were once real: The dog did bite, your parents were critical, or the robbers did attack. But to go on protecting ourselves once the situation has passed and, worse, to see the old situation where it doesn't exist are to lose choice and spontaneity. Although Ben's experience is extreme—and more difficult to work with—all of us have lost our freedom in more subtle ways. My friend Ellen's brother used to tickle her mercilessly as a child. To this day, she flinches if anyone touches her near an armpit. And when she and her husband make love—an entirely different context—she simply freezes if his hand brushes her in the wrong way. Although she doesn't consciously reject her husband, Ellen ends up feeling angry and remote as the result of a conditioned response to what is in reality a loving touch.

The mind is like the engine of a car. When it's in gear, we're carried along by its power. Angry thoughts beget further angry thoughts. Fearful thoughts gather more fear to them, and the mind takes the form of whatever it becomes absorbed in. By shifting into neutral, taking a breath, and adopting the position of the mindful observer, you can detach yourself from the mind even though it's still running. In this way the mind can ultimately become the servant rather than the master, if you learn to live in the present rather than in the past or the future. In order to do this, it's necessary to appreciate more about how the mind functions.

Healthy Mindedness

Throughout the ages, philosophers and psychologists have developed different maps of the mind. The importance of understanding mental function is that it allows cultivation of what the American physician and founder of psychology, William James, called "healthy mindedness" all the way back in the late 1890s. *The mind is a tool we use; it is not meant to be our jailer.* There are attitudes that ensure balanced mental function: cultivating mindfulness, practicing forgiveness, acting with altruism and compassion, and learning to be grateful. Similarly, there are attitudes that lead to mental confusion and stress. The Buddhists refer to three attitudes that poison the mental state: craving—our addiction to the belief that happiness is outside ourselves and that we can satisfy ourselves by pursuing objects of desire; anger—which arises when our separate sense of self tries to defend what it wants and judges people and situations harshly; and ignorance of the basic fact of life that everything is interconnected and constantly changing.

In order to take a closer look at mending the mind—creating the conditions for healthy mindedness and peace—we'll work with a simple mind map that my colleague psychotherapist Steve Maurer used to share with the participants in our Mind/Body

Programs. The map is useful because it can help you understand and use your mind to its best advantage:

The conscious mind. The sights, sounds, smells, tastes, and touch that our senses take in are the simplest forms of data we have about the world. At this level, a black dog is a black dog. It's neither scary nor pleasant. It just is. The pain of a fractured pelvis or fibromyalgia isn't bad or good. It's pure, naked sensation. When we're babies, before we develop experience and language, sense perception is our primary form of consciousness. If we're hungry or scared we cry. If we're tired, we sleep. If our bladder is full, we pee. There's no separation between perception and action and no conscious overlay or context. In some forms of meditation, including mindfulness, attention to sense perception is a primary focus. Simply closing your eyes and noticing the sensation where your feet touch the floor is a primary experience of body energy and aliveness.

The unconscious mind. Every one of our experiences is encoded as an impression—and sometimes a well-developed neural network—within the nervous system. That's why we don't have to relearn to drive a car every time we get behind the wheel. As we'll see in Chapter 6, the unconscious is a treasure trove of learning that can be drawn on to bring wisdom—or at least experience—to any situation. As we've already seen, it's also a Pandora's box of fears, disappointments, and old behavior patterns that may no longer be relevant, yet persist for better and for worse unless we're willing to engage in a program of cultivating healthy mindedness.

The intellect. This is the remarkable capacity to reason, using data both from conscious sense perceptions and from stored learnings in the unconscious. The purest form of intellect is "thinking by choice" rather than being trapped in unbidden rumination over "what ifs" and "if onlys" or blinded by desire, fear, or prejudice. The Hoffman Quadrinity Process, a week-long program of healing old patterns left from childhood, maintains that much of our afflictive inner dialogue (when we feel caught in doubt, judgment, anger, stressful thinking, fear, and confusion) is a highly patterned, repetitive type of conversation between our intellect and our unhealed emotional child. You can experiment by observing your own mind to test the validity of this assertion. When the intellect is functioning clearly, unclouded by the fear and doubt of historical patterns, the mind is in its glory, functioning in a fresh, creative way.

The ego. How would I describe myself? I'm a wife, a mother, a grandmother, a medical scientist, a psychologist, the author of many books, a seminar leader, a radio show host, and a very minor television personality. I'm a biker, a skier, a gardener, and a singer. I'm vulnerable, funny, and slightly neurotic, and I work too much. I adore my husband, my children, my grandchildren, my friends, and our dog. I'm very practical and deeply spiritual. I hope for liberation in this lifetime in its truest sense—freedom from past conditioning and union with a larger whole. *I, I, I. My, My, My. Mine, Mine, Mine.* Is this description, this self-referential litany really who I am? This is the ego certainly, but perhaps not the whole Joan. At times the ego can seem more like a Mardi Gras mask than an authentic expression of being. An identity is useful in many cases, but if you believe in it as something fixed—reified—then you become like the pillar of salt that Lot's wife turned into when she looked back at Sodom and Gomorrah, wanting to hold onto the old rather than flowing with the change that is life's real essence. Becoming fully human requires first forming an ego, then understanding it, and finally transcending it to become part of a greater reality. The latter involves *having* an ego, but not *being* an ego, allowing its wants and fears to run your life.

The four parts of the mind will be dealt with further in the chapters that follow. Since the ego is the part of the mind most constrained by fear, supporting mindless repetition of unhealthy mental patterns, it's important to understand a little bit about its development.

Development of the Ego: The Judge

The ego develops during childhood. At first the baby thinks that it's one with its mother. Later it begins to develop the sense of a separate self. If you've ever thrown up your hands in exasperation at the *no*'s of a two-year-old, you've seen the ego developing. All human beings need to know that they're persons in their own right, capable of living and creating in a way that is both morally appropriate and uniquely theirs.

The basic role of the ego is to provide our personal uniqueness with an identity through which to express itself. Unfortunately, the developing ego usually encounters a host of mixed messages that leave impressions of fear and insecurity. The child whose parents are too busy, stressed, or ignorant to provide an adequate holding environment (the kind of consistent love and care that creates basic trust in the safety of the world) develops various means of getting attention and feeling seen.

These may range from being exemplary in every way to acting out by setting fire to the house. Both behaviors are simply attempts to get what the child needs in order to survive: recognition of its inherent worthiness.

For most of us, the ego is a mixed bag. It generates some behaviors that lead to intimacy, productivity, and creativity. It generates others that create rigid thinking and barriers to being present—what is called presence. A common barrier is the armor around the heart that so many of us suffer from. Fearing abandonment and disappointment, we close ourselves off from love.

The ego expresses its insecurities through relentless judgment and comparison, trying to ensure happiness by keeping control over circumstance and people, which it perceives as separate from itself. For this reason I call the ego the Judge. It tends to split life into rigid categories—good and bad, us and them, black and white. Blindly seeking pleasure and avoiding pain, it's caught in the illusion that it must be right in order to ensure its own existence. The basic truth about reality—that everything is interconnected—is unappreciated, and as a result the afflictive emotions of fear, anger, and jealousy become ingrained habits of mind.

Going Beyond the Mind: The Witness

A baby's mind has not yet developed. It has consciousness—that is, sense perception—but attaches no meaning to perception at first. Through experience and conditioning, the other three parts of the mind are gradually built up. Out of what does the mind form? Do you cease to exist if your mind is entirely still, no longer functioning? These are questions worth considering.

Try this experiment before reading further. Since the mind speaks in words, for the next minute become the witness, the listener of your mind. Close your eyes, breath a sigh of relief, take three abdominal breaths, and listen to your mind for one minute.

What happened? You probably had one of two experiences. Either you watched your thoughts go by or, strangely, there were no thoughts at all. When Steve Maurer would suggest this exercise to our patients, they were often amazed that when they watched the mind closely, it stopped or slowed down. Steve used to say that the mind gets shy when we watch it. Usually the experience of witnessing the mind—whether the mind falls silent or keeps on running—is one of peacefulness. You don't stop existing if your mind becomes quiet. You're still aware of your own existence and your own consciousness, and that awareness is quite peaceful. Try the experiment again for a minute.

Meditation develops the ability to become aware of a completely nonjudgmental part of the mind, that of the Witness. The Witness is the part of your mind that watches—that is aware of thinking. Since the Witness is outside the partial identity we call ego, it's not caught up in judging and is thus content in any situation. Another name for the Witness is the Self, or the unconditioned mind. It's the same in everyone because it's not conditional on what our experiences have been. It exists previous to experience and the arising of the different parts of the mind. In many different psychologies and philosophies, the ego is called the self with a small *s* because it represents our own personal history, complete with all the limitations of our attitudes and fears. The Self with a big S represents completely unlimited potential.

The recognition that there's an essential similarity in every human being—that the core of each of us consists of the same consciousness—is at the heart of spiritual experience. Buddhism is a well-developed, experiential system of awakening to our true nature. Hinduism speaks in terms of the Atman, or Self, becoming one with Brahman, or Ultimate Reality. Christian mystic Father Thomas Keating, who teaches a form of meditation called Centering Prayer, speaks of dismantling the false self and discovering our true Self—what he identifies as our participation in divine being.

Systems of psychological growth have a similar end point in terms of freedom from limitation, but they often lack an orientation toward awakening to true nature. Nonetheless, when doubt and fear quiet down, we often become aware of an inner wellspring of security, compassion, peace, and joy that informs our contribution to the wholeness of life. Regardless of concepts, all maps of the mind—whether psychological or spiritual—lead to actualizing the potential that dwells within as our full humanity. Whether one's orientation is to self-realization, awakening, divine union, or simply to wholeness and inner peace, learning to disengage from judgment and enter the larger space of the Witness—in which we sense our interconnectedness with a larger whole—is an important skill to develop.

One of our cancer patients at the clinic, a woman named Mary, told her mind/body group a beautiful story. She'd known about her ovarian cancer for just a few months and, having completed surgery, was midway into a short course of chemotherapy. She and her husband decided to drive to the Adirondack Mountains

to rest from the strain of the previous months. They were sitting by a clear mountain lake on an early spring day in the late afternoon, listening mindfully to the songs of the birds and the sounds of the wind. The setting sun was fanning out into a panoramic show of reds and purples that shimmered as it reflected on the still surface of the water. Suddenly, Mary lost the usual perception of herself looking *at* the water. Instead she felt a powerful experience of being at *one* with the water, the birds, the sky, the earth, and her husband. The boundaries between herself and her perceptions had melted away. Later Mary realized that the experience had lasted for about ten minutes, but it had seemed timeless.

Struggling to put her emotional state into words, Mary focused on transcendent peace, at-one-ment with the universe, and total love. She went on to say that she now felt less fearful about the cancer because she'd experienced firsthand that human consciousness is not limited to the individual. The other group members were quite moved by her description, which triggered memories of similar, though less intense, experiences they had had at different times in their lives.

Surrendering to What Is

One of my patients named John, a man who had gone blind because of his diabetes, once commented that being blind wasn't his problem. John's problem was that he couldn't let go of wishing that he weren't blind. As soon as his mind began relating to the desire for things to be different, he began to feel angry and frustrated, which made him feel tense and irritable. His frustrated feelings reengaged stored memories of other times when he had felt helpless and angry. John's wish was to break out of that mind-set and learn to live with his blindness.

John was caught in the most familiar bind of them all: wishing for life to be different. That's the essence of suffering. I don't mean that we shouldn't have hopes and dreams, and work toward a better future for ourselves and the world. But the past, and the moment you're experiencing right now, can't be changed. They are what they are by definition. When we resist reality—"It's rain-ing. Why does it always rain on my day off? I hate the rain!"—our whining and complaining leads to misery rather than peace. When we fight with reality only one thing is certain. *We will lose.* The path to peace lies in surrender to what is.

How many times has your mind told you that you could be happy *if* you lost ten pounds? made more money? had your health? Then, even if these things come to pass, you just move on to the next set of conditions for happiness. The conditions are like the proverbial carrot that dangles in front of the donkey. You never reach them.

Happiness can occur only at the moment that desires cease. At that time the mind is still. It's not thinking, not wanting or fearing; it's totally absorbed and attentive. Can you remember the experience of being really thirsty on a hot summer's day and hav-ing the relief of taking a drink? Every time the mind is completely absorbed—engaged and mindful—it grows still, and you auto-matically experience the background of unconditioned con-sciousness—the Self—that is always there but is usually hidden behind the ripples of the mind. *Because gratification of a desire leads to the temporary stilling of the mind and the experience of the peaceful, joyful Self, it's no wonder that we get hooked on thinking that happiness comes from the satisfaction of desires. This is the meaning of the old adage "Joy is not in things; it is in us."*

Although getting something we want or avoiding something we don't can give us peace briefly, it never lasts. The mind is like a junkie—on the prowl for its next hit of peacefulness by looking to satisfy a desire. Between satisfactions, the experience for many of us may be generally unpleasant. True peacefulness comes from abandoning the illusion that satisfying desires brings pleasure. It is called even-mindedness. In that state, you regard every moment as an opportunity to live fully, to be aware. Instead of doing the dishes with the attitude that life is on hold until the unpleasant chore is over, you can choose to do the dishes mindfully, observing the sensations of the water, the bubbles, the feel of the plates. In the state of mindful observation, there are no more judgments about pleasant or unpleasant. The mind grows still, and you can feel the contentment of the Self.

A woman named Sabrina, whom I'd taught basic meditation, called me a week later in a panic. Sabrina's mind had become very still during a practice session, and her breath had become so slow that it hardly moved. Time lost its meaning, her body filled with exquisitely pleasurable sensations, and she felt what she could only describe as total joy and peace—unconditional love and a unity with all things. Descriptions of such states are common if you read the lives of the saints or the poetry of ecstatic mystical poets like Rumi. The problem Sabrina had, though, was getting trapped in the wheel of desires. On the one hand, she feared the "what if" such an experience led into other states that might not be so pleasant—the old fear of losing control. But when the experience didn't repeat itself, that fear gave way to "if only" it would happen again. Sabrina judged her other attempts to meditate as lackluster by comparison. The experience she desired couldn't happen, of course, as long as she was holding on to *making* it happen, because the mind was stuck in judging, so that the unconditioned state of presence was blocked.

I gave Sabrina the same advice that a meditation teacher once gave me: "Don't make any appointments and you won't have any disappointments." This means adopting a state of even-mindedness where you are free to "go with the flow," learning from whatever circumstances arise. Alice's attitude toward her recovery from brain damage is a great example of even-mindedness. In taking things as they unfolded, she avoided the inevitable suffering of "if only" and "what if," finding a powerful teacher in what could have been cause for suffering.

Finding peace of mind requires learning to let go. Developing the habit of taking a breath and backing up into the position of the Witness—the observing Self—is a time-tested way for learning to be mindfully present to life. Breathing consciously, while *noticing* that you're experiencing anger—without any attempt to change it, but simply being curious about it—is mindfulness. Being so stuck in the experience of anger that you're overcome by it is suffering. The highest ideal of self-understanding comes when a person's ego has retired to the extent that praise and blame are treated equally. There's no puffing up if things go well, and no shriveling up if things go poorly. This is surely a lofty ideal, but working on it is the privilege we have as human beings, and the path to healthy mindedness, compassion, and interior freedom.

SUGGESTIONS FOR THE READER

Continue watching your mind, both during meditation and during the day. Identify the kinds of desires, the "if onlys," that separate you from being happy now, and the "what ifs" that could deprive you of happiness later. You may find that your ego self revolves around a few repetitive concerns. Write these down. When they occur, congratulate yourself for becoming aware of them. Practice using your breathing as a reminder to let them go. Sometimes it helps to write your anxieties down on a pad so that you can take appropriate action on them at a time that you set aside for that purpose. There's no point worrying about cleaning the house or writing a report or having a conversation before it happens. Do things as a matter of conscious choice, chipping away at unconscious conditioning.

Choose at least one activity each day to carry out mindfully—with your full attention, like a meditation. If you're chopping vegetables, chop vegetables. Absorb yourself in the colors, the textures, the motions. If you're drying off after a shower, just dry yourself. It feels great. Ram Dass, the former Harvard psychologist who spent years studying consciousness, sums up mindfulness in the message of his perennially popular book *Be Here Now.* Put up a few signs around the house as reminders. The practice is easy; it's remembering to do it that's hard.

Don't let your ego bully you and scare you off. Old patterns are hard to change, and usually, as soon as you try, they seem to get stronger in response. This is natural. Many people think they are worse off than before when they start to notice how their mind works. You are no worse off; you've simply realized what goes on inside. Awareness is the first step to making new choices. It's worth the temporary discomfort to get to know yourself.

Use mindfulness to cope with pain and anxiety. I discussed how to do that in the last chapter. Keep trying. If you feel anxious feelings arising inside, try to witness them. Instead of getting stuck in judging, be the observer. By not engaging the mind in battle, by watching and letting thoughts go, it will soon become quiet. One very anxious patient, Elizabeth, was a twenty-eight-year-old housewife. Her frequent panic attacks were so severe that she thought she was dying. Then one day she said to herself, "Okay, so I'm dying. Do I want to die all full of fear and uptight, or do I want to die peacefully?" She dropped back into her breathing and began to witness the physical sensation of panic. Soon she began to feel peaceful. Needless to say, she didn't die. Since no medication helped Elizabeth with her panic attacks at that time (there are several that might help now), she believed that mindfulness was her only resource. That motivation was important in helping her apply the lessons of healthy mindedness when she needed to.

CHAPTER 5

Mind Traps

Outwitting the Dirty Tricks
Department of the Mind

Two monks were walking by a river at daybreak in the early spring. Swollen with melted snow, the river coursed above its banks, immersing the local footbridge, the only crossing for miles in either direction, under two feet of water. A young woman in a silk dress stood by the riverbank, terrified of the rushing water. Seeing the monks, she flashed them a look of pleading. Without a word, the first monk scooped her up in his arms, held her aloft as he struggled across the submerged bridge, and set her down on the far bank. The two monks then continued walking in silence until sunset, when the vows of their order allowed them to speak.

"How could you have picked up that woman?" sputtered the second monk, his eyes blazing with anger. "You know very well that we are prohibited from even thinking about women, let alone touching them. You sullied your honor. You are a disgrace to the whole order." He shook his fist at his companion.

"Venerable brother," said the first monk, "I put that woman down on the other side of the river at sunrise. It is you who have been carrying her around all day."

My students always laugh at this old Zen teaching story, because it's so typical of the way the mind holds onto a situation, creating suffering long after the incident has passed. It's much harder to be the first monk, putting down the burden by the edge of the river so that it doesn't become a problem that's carried through the day or even for life. Although it's easy to see that letting go is much more comfortable than holding on, how can letting go be learned?

Learning to Let Go

In Southeast Asia, hunters use a clever trap for catching monkeys. The hunter hollows out a pumpkinlike gourd, taking care to leave the shell intact except for a hole just large enough for him to push a banana inside. By and by a monkey will happen along, discover the banana, and stick its hand in the gourd to get it. As soon as the monkey clutches its hand around the banana, it's trapped—hand and banana will not fit through the hole. The poor monkey seals its own fate because its mind cannot give up the idea of grabbing the fruit. The monkey can't let go and is quite literally a prisoner of its own mind.

Human beings, unlike monkeys, have *awareness* and *choice* at their disposal, the two keys to escape from any bind. The monkey's first obstacle is that it doesn't recognize that holding onto the banana is the source of its problem. Without some awareness of what has happened, the monkey can't choose to let go. Like our primate brethren, we frequently fail to recognize that within our minds is the power to let go and create a different situation. Instead we find it easier to place the blame on the pumpkin or any other immediate circumstance we associate with our suffering.

Some years back I was standing at the stove preparing string beans, the last step before dinner, when my fifteen-year-old son, Justin, entered the kitchen. He was a wrestler, and when he stood at the open refrigerator as a teenager, I sometimes felt as though he could inhale the food right off the shelves.

"Dinner's almost ready," I said, but he took out an apple anyway.

He leaned against the counter, eating his apple while I frantically raced to snap the tips off the string beans before the water boiled. "You know, Mom, I'll bet Aunt Sandy spends a hundred dollars a week on cabs. Why doesn't she buy her own car like the rest of the world?"

"It's not that easy," I said. I moved around him to the sink and scooped the rest of the raw beans out of the colander. "She lives in the city and she'd have to rent a parking space. That's expensive. Plus, there are loan payments, insurance, and gas, not to mention general maintenance and repairs—it could cost her as much as taking cabs. Besides, she *likes* taxis."

"But she could get a great used car for six grand—that's only about ninety bucks a month." He picked up a string bean, snapped it in two, and began tossing the halves from one palm to the other.

"Well, Justin, maybe Aunt Sandy wouldn't settle for such an old car." The water was just starting to bubble. I picked up the beans in both hands. "A good used car can easily cost fifteen thousand or much more even." The beans hit the water with a soft splash.

He snorted. "What a waste!"

"It's not a waste," I said. "Which costs more—a cheap car that falls apart in three or four years or an expensive car that lasts ten?"

He made a sour face. "You don't have to spend a fortune to get a good car." He dropped the two halves of the string bean on the counter.

When the pot came back to a rolling boil, I waited thirty seconds, then turned down the gas. I could feel Justin watching me, wondering how far he could push his dear old mother.

The handle of the pot was still hot and I grabbed it without thinking. I yelped. My fingers flew off the handle. In a second I had pushed past Justin and was running cold water over my singed fingertips. "It's not that important! What makes you such an expert on cars, anyway? Why don't you make yourself useful for a change instead of worrying about how everybody else is spending their money?"

Justin stared at me. There are times when I look at my son and I see my own startled reflection. I laughed. Why were we so concerned about a hypothetical car that no one was even planning to buy?

Justin pulled the pot off the burner and nudged me away from the sink. "Look out or you'll really get burned."

I listened to what was really going on in my mind, the real subject of the conversation. It wasn't cars, of course. Both my son and I clung tenaciously to hidden agendas. The real conversation was a battle of who-knows-best. Both of us were stuck with our hands in the pumpkin, neither willing to admit that the other could have a valid point of view.

Most parents with teenage children know this game all too well. The conversation in my own mind was about being in control, about not being wrong. Only by taking a breath and dropping into the position of observer, the Witness, as we discussed in the previous chapter, could I have the awareness that afforded me some choice. There was no one to blame and nothing to argue about.

"It's pretty ridiculous for us to be standing here making up a car that Aunt Sandy isn't planning to buy anyway," I said.

Justin sheepishly shook the beans in the colander, emptied them into a bowl, and said he'd go call his father and brother for dinner. Only when I pointed out the humor of the debate could we both let go of it and move on to other things. "She'd probably want a Porsche," he finished, smiling, as he left the kitchen.

Listening to what was really going on in my mind—the conversation behind the conversation—I recognized my favorite mind trap: needing to be right. Whenever I become aware of it, I remember a brief reminder from psychiatrist Gerald Jampolsky: "Would I rather be happy or would I rather be right?" Yet it's usually hard to relinquish deeply held patterns of behavior. I've often been trapped in my own desire to be right, caught up in the belief that if only others would acknowledge *my* position, then I could let go. I postpone my own happiness. Sound familiar?

Anger, anxiety, and sadness, alone or in combination, are usually the fruits of clinging to a viewpoint or an agenda. Negative emotions arise from past associations that repeat themselves in our minds and from the response of others who become annoyed with our inflexibility. This chapter explores the part of the mind that makes it hard to let go. Ideally, by understanding the "dirty tricks department" of the mind, you'll gain insight into how your mind really works. Awareness is the first step to a healthier life. It's a mental stretching that limbers up your perceptions, making you loose enough to let go and thus allowing an element of creative choice to expand possibilities.

The Dirty Tricks Department of the Mind

In Chapter 4, we discussed the four parts of the mind. You probably remember the ego, which I characterized as a merciless judge who forever divides the world into good and bad, vigilantly sizing things up to make sure that we get what we want and avoid what we don't want. In the process, there's a trade-off. We won't be happy, the ego says, unless we get what we want, but the ego often sees the world in terms of scarcity, danger, and loss. This view taints with fear even those moments of satisfaction—since some unforeseen danger may come along and ruin our happiness. This is how many people think. Like Esau, we sell our birthright for a bowl of porridge. The porridge is the trap: "I can be happy if I get what I want and avoid what I don't want." Our birthright is the inner Witness—the unconditioned awareness that is already fulfilled and happy, *regardless* of outer circumstances.

All of the mind's machinations spring from this single mistake. Our ego churns out an endless stream of mental movies, glittering images of our likes and dislikes, and the more we grasp or recoil at these images, the more estranged we become from our Witness, our only real source of peace.

As we saw in Chapter 4, most of the old baggage that gets transferred onto immediate experience contains stored memories of the ego's basic desires: getting what we want and avoiding what we don't want. The ego, confusing happiness with the fulfillment of these desires, perpetuates our suffering by creating a series of mind traps based on fear. Ignorance, the ego's dynamic, is our primary obstacle to freedom, our greatest hindrance to letting go.

Getting What You Want

Wanting things is a natural part of life. Setting goals and working toward them enhance creativity and invention. The desire to change things activates progress. Wanting, per se, isn't the root difficulty; it's the pernicious attitude that we can't possibly be happy unless we satisfy a certain craving. I once had a patient who had recently divorced. He was so convinced that his happiness depended on being in love that he was miserable without a relationship. His misery, of course, manifested itself as a host of uninvited problems. He became an insomniac, which left him irritable and tense. Tired, he stopped playing racquetball and tennis and became even more tense. Desperate, he tried eating and drinking the problem away, in the process loathing himself more and more. In due course, he developed ulcers and severe headaches. Ironically, by identifying happiness exclusively with a relationship, and not as something within himself, he undermined his chances of attracting a suitable mate.

We suffer to the degree that we make our desires central to our happiness. As my son Justin's sixteenth birthday approached, he got increasingly desperate to own a car. Suddenly there was no other way to get to school, to see his friends, even to exist. He poured every spare moment into fulfilling this desire. His first purchase, a forty-dollar heap, held together for two weeks after his sixteenth birthday. The very night of its collapse into scrap metal, he set out to get another one. This car lasted four days, until its collision with a school bus on a snowy road. In the following month, while waiting for the insurance settlement, Justin slowly realized that life could go on. A car was not the final referee of his happiness.

Many situations, unfortunately, are not so clear. In marriage, for example, hanging onto the idea that we can't be happy until our spouse behaves like Prince or Princess Charming blocks our appreciation of his or her good qualities. We stay stuck in longing for what we can't have.

Deferring happiness until any condition is met—a new job, a new relationship, a new possession—leads to suffering. In clinging to our desires, we send ourselves a strong statement that things are not okay right now. As life goes on, the feeling of dissatisfaction keeps us hooked to our wants, preventing us from letting go and enjoying the present moment.

Remember your first apartment? Bliss! A place of your own at last. But soon you begin to notice the flaws. The rooms are *so* small. There's never enough hot water. The upstairs neighbors practice their salsa moves at 2 a.m. Before long you want to move. You get a bigger apartment. Home free, finally. Until the couple next door has a baby, and the cycle starts all over again. There's never an end to wanting. Whenever a desire masquerades as the thing that separates you from happiness, the rest of life drops into the background. Your desire has become a prison locking you out of life.

Getting What You Don't Want

The other kind of desire we discussed in Chapter 4 is the wish to avoid getting something we don't want. Mentally, each of us creates a cauldron seething with life's potentially painful experiences, and since each of us is unique, the imaginary disasters that bubble to the surface differ with each of us. For one person, the ultimate terror may be a lonely widowhood; another's demon is the thought of losing a job. At an extreme, such worries can totally paralyze their victims.

When my own boys were young, my mother used to reminisce frequently about the kidnapping of the Lindbergh baby nearly fifty years before. My grandfather apparently lost sleep for weeks, fretting about the possible abduction of my older brother, his first grandchild. Eventually he installed locks on every window in my parents' house. Most of the time, the ego's bullying projections never materialize, but that doesn't stop our apprehension. The great sage who writes teabag aphorisms got it partly right: "Worry is the interest paid on a debt before it comes due." And in so many cases, it never comes due.

Mind Traps: Double Jeopardy

The ego tries to stop our suffering by explaining why we hurt. Dividing the world into good and bad, the ego naturally connects painful events with something bad, and the first place it looks is the storehouse of negative opinions about ourselves and the world that we've spent a lifetime gathering. Instead of exploring the situation at hand, the ego grabs the solution it knows best: unfounded opinion. The ego hammers these negative beliefs into *mind traps,* mental grillwork that cuts us off from an accurate view of life. Without clarity we have no awareness, and without awareness we have no choices. We end up suffering instead of finding liberation.

Anguish is only part of the price we pay for letting our thinking lapse into mind traps. Certain traps, particularly the ones connected with negative personal beliefs, disillusion, and despair, increase our physical vulnerability to disease.

You may remember the damaging effects of helplessness described in Chapter 1. Martin Seligman, author of many books, including *The Optimistic Child* and *Learned Optimism,* and the founder of the positive psychology movement, has performed many experiments that demonstrate how most human beings, when consistently placed in situations over which they feel they have no control, are permeated by a sense of helplessness that often extends beyond the specific event. Seligman and collaborators found that if they deprived people of the ability to reduce the noise level in a lab, about two-thirds of them later failed to adjust an irritatingly bright light, although they had the power to do so. They believed themselves helpless.

Seligman paid very careful attention to his subjects' thoughts about unpleasant experiences, and he found his group divided into optimists and pessimists. Those who were pessimists became helpless. Pessimistic thinking about unwanted experiences revolves around three attitudes, all of which begin with the letter *P* (and all of which, we shall see, also characterize mind traps). Pessimists take things *personally.* They tend to blame themselves for adverse occurrences; they often characterize such circumstances as *permanent,* lasting indefinitely; and they conclude that they're generally incompetent—that their helplessness is *pervasive.*

A pessimist, should his car skid into a school bus on a snowy day, might think about the event in this way: "I'm such a lousy driver (personal). I'll never learn to drive safely (permanent). Every time I try something new, I screw it up (pervasive)."

The optimist, on the other hand, might blame the snowy roads, maybe the other driver, or poor visibility. Although he might be inclined to take responsibility, he wouldn't take the blame. Nor would he take the accident as an indication he'd never learn to drive safely ("I'm just a beginner, and beginners have to expect a banged fender once in a while. I'll have to be extra careful until I'm a little more practiced"). Last of all, the optimist wouldn't read the accident as a sign that he was a terminal screwup.

Buddhist and Hindu philosophical systems offer amazingly well-developed tools for observing the mind and avoiding the mental activities that cause suffering. The *Yogasutras* of Patanjali, an ancient guide to spiritual practice, states in its opening sentence that "Yoga is the stilling of the modifications of the mind." These modifications, of course, are the constant, inner chatter and repetitive negative statements that sap so much of our energy. The point of meditation, as originally taught in spiritual traditions, was to achieve awareness of the mind so that thinking could be a matter of choice rather than of habit.

The art of stilling the mind, like all arts, takes time and practice. The information on mind traps is enough for you to get started, a very rudimentary map of a complicated territory. Reread the instructions in Chapter 2 on meditation. Remember to be the observer. Meditation is a microcosm of how to use your knowledge of mind traps. In meditation you remember for a few seconds to follow your breathing, or repeat a word or phrase, and identify with the Inner Self or Witness rather than with the mind. Then a sticky thought floats by and catches your attention. Off you go on a wild goose chase of associations until you finally remember to be aware ("Oh! There I go—thinking again"), letting go and returning to the breath. Discerning mind traps is similar. Usually we completely identify with the mind's contents. Then we remember to step back and observe, asking ourselves if our thoughts resemble any of the mind traps. Inevitably, the emotion of the moment will sweep us away again. Still, a consistent effort to observe, to remember the Witness, will eventually bear fruit. *Eventually you'll recognize that you have thoughts, but that you're not your thoughts.*

Attuning yourself to the devious ways the ego works gives you the power to listen to yourself in a new way, to unmask the hidden staging behind the drama of events. Recognizing the pattern of a mind trap in your response to a particular experience won't bring instant release. Mind traps are strong precisely because we've been practicing them for years, and undoing them takes concentration and an almost heroic effort. Awareness is the price of happiness, no matter how challenging in the beginning. Only when you can identify where your ego traps are can you let go and begin to make choices based on a more realistic appraisal of circumstances.

Let's begin our discussion of mind traps with a commonplace occurrence, a domestic squabble that ruins the day. Listen carefully to Jennifer's thoughts and try to sort them into *opinion* (unfounded belief concocted in her mind) and *fact*. Opinions, rather than events or situations, cause most of our suffering.

It's Friday, 7:30 a.m. Both Jennifer and John are rushing to leave for work. It's Jennifer's turn to make breakfast this morning and she's gotten off on the wrong foot by oversleeping fifteen minutes. She tosses two bagels into the toaster and heads for the bathroom. A few minutes later the aroma of incinerating bagels interrupts her application of eyeliner. She rushes out to the kitchen. "It's too late," John says, holding the smoking bagels under the faucet. "So much for breakfast."

Jennifer gives him a poisonous glare. "We wouldn't be out of bagels if *somebody* had done the shopping."

"We wouldn't need more bagels if you'd gotten the toaster fixed on Tuesday, like you said you would. Besides, *somebody* was working on your car during all his free time, if you remember correctly."

Jennifer snaps that her car is running worse than ever. John tells her to fix it herself next time. They storm out of the house, and both of them nurse a grudge for the rest of the day.

Let's follow Jennifer's thoughts as her ego trundles out the heavy guns, the six most common mind traps. Bear in mind that although we're examining the traps in order, the mind is never as tidy; thinking jumps from one trap to another, according to our idiosyncrasies.

Trap 1: Personal Put Downs

Jennifer: "I'm *so* scatterbrained. I never get organized to get out of here on time. Things are always falling apart around me. I suppose I shouldn't expect things to be different. I'm a lousy cook anyway."

The heart of this trap is a mean, self-deprecating opinion of oneself without the evidence to back it up. Jennifer, in fact, is a vice president of a large Boston bank. She obviously didn't climb the corporate ladder by behaving like a scatterbrain. She makes her bad situation worse by telling herself that she'll never get out of this bind. Like one of Seligman's helpless subjects, she assumes that the situation will last forever and that it reflects the tenor of her entire life. Yet everything about Jennifer's kitchen—pots hanging overhead within easy reach and professional utensils lined upright in a magnetic rack by the counter—epitomizes neatness and organization. Contrary to her internal statement, things in her life almost never "fall apart." Jennifer's mind has cooked up "scatterbrained," a negative personal belief that doesn't even remotely correspond to how most people would characterize her.

When you can't explain away your problems, it's easy to assume you're inadequate, easy to dredge up some fabricated weakness. Snapping at a child and then concluding, "Well, I guess I'm just a rotten parent," doesn't bring any awareness into the situation. Such statements never ask *why* you behaved as you did. Perhaps you were stressed at work and were taking it out on your child; or perhaps you were repeating what your father did to you. Honest inquiry, without blame, is the beginning of insight that leads to more skillful behavior and a more peaceful heart. Self-blame that's no more than a label, rather than an occasion for inquiry, shuts the door on learning. Personal put downs revolve around badness, around your not being good enough. They just assume you're at fault, which is not at all the same as *taking responsibility for understanding the situation.* Trap 1 completely dismisses your personal power to learn and grow, and your freedom of choice.

People who fall into this first mind trap often lacerate their self-esteem with distorted images of their bodies as well. My friend and colleague Steve Maurer used to tell the story of a friend who was commonly regarded as the most beautiful woman in his social circle. She had a truly distinguished nose, similar to Sophia Loren's. One day she appeared in bandages, announcing that she'd gotten her nose straightened. All her life she'd thought her nose was ugly, an opinion that literally flew in the face of reality.

At an extreme, viewing the body in negative terms can lead to bulimia, to anorexia, or even to death. Although eating disorders are usually associated with females, they're often present, though hidden, in men as well. Witness the emaciated male runner. A growing health consciousness unfortunately encourages unrealistic expectations of our bodies. New diets, video workouts, and health clubs spring up every day, each touting our potential for the perfect shape. A colleague of mine returned from a two-week vacation looking rather drawn and thin. Concerned, I commented on her loss of weight. To my surprise, she interpreted this as a compliment. "Thanks, Joan. After all, in our society you can never be too rich or too thin."

Not everyone manifests this trap in such dramatic physical terms. Yet the thoughts of its victims steam down the rails of the same track—a conviction, first of all, that you're bad and, second, that you'll never be good enough (good enough for *what* is a question with a thousand individual answers). Under an assault from Trap 1, your self-esteem can erode into nothing.

Trap 2: The "Shoulds"

Jennifer: "John shouldn't have snapped at me like that. Burning the bagels made me want to crawl back into bed and start the day over. He should have given me some support and love. Husbands and wives are supposed to support each other. I thought that's what marriage was all about. Come to think of it, our marriage isn't what it should be."

Should is a code word with the force of society behind it. All of us hold beliefs about how life should proceed. Everyone benefits if we agree to stop at red lights, honor the Golden Rule, and forbid the use of guns to settle arguments. In everyday parlance, however, we use *should* to express displeasure at not getting what we want. Jennifer tells herself she wouldn't be suffering over the bagel fiasco if she had a more supportive husband. It's quite possible for someone to burn the breakfast bagels and still be happy—hardly giving it a thought—but Jennifer has cut herself off from this possibility. *I won't be happy,* she tells herself, *unless life meets these conditions.*

Hurling an angry broadside of *should*s at another person only provokes more suffering. *Should* implies that you're perfect and the other person is to blame. We can hardly blame John if his first response is to defend himself, and most likely he'll fire off an irate counterattack. *Unless John behaves as he should, then it's his fault I'm unhappy* (or so Jennifer believes).

In a variation of Trap 2, Jennifer could have turned her wrath against herself: *I should have known better than to try toasting the* *bagels and applying my makeup at the same time. Should*s serve only to plunge us deeper into our bad feelings about ourselves, feelings that easily boil over into anger—as they did for John and Jennifer on the morning of the bagel fiasco.

Trap 3: Anger and Blame

Jennifer: "So ask yourself, who does the lion's share of the work around here? John hasn't the slightest idea about all I do to make this place run smoothly. He thinks he's Mr. Sensitive if he offers to toast the bagels alternate mornings. Big deal. The creep can toast his own bagels from now on."

Of the traps we've examined thus far, Number 3 has the most zing to it. The defeatist, helpless attitude of the first trap gave way to irritation in Trap 2, as Jennifer's mental conversation shifted to *should*s. In the third trap, it escalates to outright anger. Anger can attach to anything—to another person, to rules, to a particular institution (work, government, religion, even the PTA), or to life itself. In this case it attached to John. Whenever we think that another person's behavior is responsible for our happiness—and are then disappointed because we don't get what we want—anger and blame are a likely response. Stuck in Trap 3, Jennifer inflates her anger into blame and attaches it to John, thereby asserting her own innocence.

This kind of thinking leads to separation—both from the recipient of the blame and from ourselves. In the grip of Trap 3, we're absolutely convinced of the rightness of our position, and nothing can make us change our minds. Being right becomes more important than anything else. Adolescent children often have this perspective, which is a natural part of growing up. An adolescent forges his own identity by separating from his parents, sometimes rebelliously: "It's my ear and I'll wear a safety pin through it if I want to!"

In an adult, such insistence on being right traps one into a turtle's-eye view of the world and reduces the realm of choice to a slit of daylight glimpsed between halves of a shell. Safe, but with limited options. When Justin and I discussed his aunt's buying a car, we could have terminated the conversation in Trap 3 language, each of us withdrawing behind our opposing convictions of rightness. Communication would have stopped. Awareness would have stopped. Choice would have stopped. Marriages turn arid and die when husband and wife make a habit of having too many conversations in this trap. Relying on anger and blame to create a sense of independence does more than just cut off relationships; it can lead to the quirky antisocial behavior that expresses contempt for society's rules or, if carried one step further, contempt for society's laws, or criminality.

In the case of Justin and me, we were able to let go because I identified the trap, took responsibility for my behavior, and used the interaction as a way to stimulate awareness in both of us. Neither one of us had to be wrong.

Trap 4: Rationalization

Jennifer: "John must be really tired this morning. That's why he snapped at me. I'll bet he was tossing and turning all night because of that tennis elbow. That must be it. I know that if I don't sleep well, I blow things way out of proportion. He'll probably apologize tonight."

Rationalization, Trap 4, is the process of assembling an explanation of events that satisfies us intellectually because it seems to conform to our perceptions. In fact, we often invent feelings or even whole identities for other people. What a surprise when they behave like themselves instead of our fantasies of them. Jennifer has no reliable indication that John lost any sleep or was bothered in the slightest by his tennis elbow. Nevertheless, they did have an unpleasant exchange this morning, and Jennifer needs to find a plausible explanation.

Like all traps, rationalization has no foundation in actual experience. The bits and pieces of information that go into its construction are frequently projections of our own thinking. We attribute to others our own modes of feeling and acting. Since no two people think exactly alike, this strategy fails. We can always intuit when we're rationalizing. If Jennifer believed her explanation, she could let go of the dogfight over the bagels. But because she instinctively recognizes that John's tennis elbow isn't the real issue, she still feels terrible. Whenever you devise a solution that *sounds* like common sense, but your head and your heart can't come together on it, you're in Trap 4.

Trap 5: Disillusionment

Jennifer hurries home early from the bank, then remembers that John will be at an office meeting until seven-thirty. She mixes herself a martini, collapses into an armchair with her drink, and reaches for the pack of cigarettes she bought on the way home. She quit smoking three years ago, but there's nothing like a smoke and a drink when you've got the blues.

Jennifer: "I might as well face it. Things will never change between us. If we can't get along after seven years of marriage, how can we even think about having children? Maybe I'm just not cut out for marriage. Maybe I ought to get a divorce."

Disillusionment sets in when the other traps just aren't up to the job. We tried, right? We did our best, and it just wasn't good enough. If the other traps don't satisfy us, we seek some temporary escape—a drink, a cigarette, a new pair of shoes—something to keep the failure at bay.

Jennifer sips on her martini, raking back through her marriage, her previous encounters with other men, stitching together a picture of incompetence to validate her sense of having blown it with John. Notice how she piggybacks her disillusionment onto the powerless, personal put downs of Trap 1: "I'm just not cut out for marriage" (in other words, she's no good at it).

Wallowing in self-pity and self-blame, Jennifer *thinks* she knows why she's stuck in her present situation—she's not good enough, or John's not good enough, or any of the other reasons we've explored in previous traps—but her reasoning has no basis in reality. Thinking she knows the answer when she doesn't places her in a very dangerous position because it shuts the door on an honest inquiry—asking the questions—that might reveal other, more realistic possibilities.

Trap 6: Despair

Jennifer: "John's abusing me—it's the story of my entire miserable life. Just give me any situation and I guarantee to mess it up.

They'll probably fire me for screwing up that big account at the bank today. My back hurts and I've got a pounding headache. About the only thing that would help now is another drink."

Alcoholism, drug addiction, and a host of other self-destructive behaviors, including suicide, are common answers to despair. Paradoxically, intense misery may be just the motivation we need to reexamine things. Mythologies of every culture contain the tale of a hero who triumphs only in the face of extreme defeat or a close encounter with death. Consider the phoenix that rises from its own ashes and the myth of Oedipus. The Oedipus tale is usually presented in its truncated form, ending with the hero's self-inflicted blindness. In other versions Oedipus' suffering teaches him compassion, allowing him first to regain his throne and then elevating him into the pantheon of the gods. In the longer version Oedipus is an archetype of crucifixion and resurrection, not the guilt-ridden servant of unpredictable fate. The Chinese word for crisis combines the characters for *danger* and *opportunity*. No society exists without this pattern deeply embedded in its consciousness.

Jennifer has not yet reached this point of extreme self-disillusionment. Perhaps instead of a drink, she settles for a nap. She can't sleep her problem away, but a little bit of peace from her destructive chain of thought is probably her best temporary solution. Naps, like meditation, allow you to let go of obsessive thoughts. She wakes up feeling refreshed; some perspective has returned. In the next part of the chapter we'll take a look at some of the ways she can expand her awareness and avoid falling into mind traps.

The Three Levels of Understanding

Level 1: The Beginner's Mind

Jennifer: "Whew, what a crazy day. I don't know how these tiffs get started or why I get so bent out of shape. You'd think I'd have more answers, but I guess I don't. All I know is that we fight more and more. I really don't understand why. What's this all about anyway?"

Understanding begins with an admission of our ignorance. A Zen story about a college professor speaks directly to this point. The professor becomes curious about the reputation of an old monk, revered for his wisdom, and decides to pay him a visit. The monk welcomes the professor to the temple, invites him inside, and installs him on a comfortable cushion.

"Do you like tea?" the monk asks, passing the professor a cup. The professor nods, as the monk pours a thin stream of tea from a heavy iron kettle. The liquid quickly rises to within an inch of the brim and the professor glances upward. The monk continues to pour. The tea rises to the brim and flows over the edge, but the monk keeps pouring.

The professor leaps to his feet, to avoid getting covered with spilled tea, yelping. "What are you doing?"

The monk pauses, dries the outside of the cup, and then offers it to the professor. "This teacup is like your mind. You can't hear anything new because it's already full."

As long as we're convinced that we know the cause of our suffering, evidence to the contrary, we're like the professor. Without letting go of old explanations, we can't open ourselves to other possibilities. Jennifer takes her first step toward understanding when she acknowledges the futility of her so-called solutions.

After a disagreeable exchange, sincerely admitting that you don't know how it came about helps to dismiss canned explanations, the negative opinions and blame, and makes you more receptive to unexplored possibilities.

Suzuki Roshi, the great Zen master, summed it up: "In the beginner's mind there are endless possibilities; in the expert's there are few." He exhorted his students to cherish the suppleness they brought to meditation as beginners, the openness that they could have only when they acknowledged that they didn't know what they were doing. If you want to stop suffering, you have to approach your problem with an empty teacup, with the mind of a beginner.

Level 2: Taking Responsibility

Jennifer: "I wonder if something in *my* behavior made John snap at me. Lately I've noticed that the times he gets angry are when I'm already feeling bad."

Without resorting to blame, Jennifer accepts that her own behavior may be contributing to her marital difficulties. She notices a pattern—a connection between John's anger and her own self-doubts. A breakthrough like this becomes possible only after you jettison all of your previously cherished opinions. An obvious pattern reveals itself only when you're clear enough to see it. Accepting responsibility for your behavior is the opposite of blaming yourself; it implies a faith in your ability to change, to transcend the negative thinking of mind traps.

Also, by thinking in terms of her behavior, instead of blame, Jennifer automatically lowers the emotional stakes of the encounter. She can discuss her observations with John and enlist his aid in probing her recent insight. They're still a long way from understanding, but they're becoming aware, trying to shift their roles from victims to observers. She and John decide that if they can't maintain their new perspective—trying to be more aware of their thinking and communicating about it openly—they'll try couples therapy. Perhaps their most important insight extends far beyond their present difficulties. That is, they don't have to follow the same mindless pattern in their relationship; they can change.

Level 3: Wisdom

Understanding is progressive. We have to work at it. No one can undo the habits of a lifetime without wrestling with those habits again and again and again. I've presented a model of understanding in three levels to give you a sense of direction and because each stage of understanding builds on its predecessor. Unraveling any negative encounter, with ourselves or others, first requires a sense of perspective. That's why, psychologically speaking, you're asked to clear the decks of your opinions in Level 1. The next stage prepares you for new insight. Taking responsibility for your actions is another way of expressing your commitment to change. Level 3, then, represents the insight that arises from a calm, blame-free perspective. Every situation, naturally, has its own teaching. Wisdom, unlike rationalization, always feels like relief. Once you understand that your goal is to understand rather than accuse, your mind will come to your aid.

Jennifer, taking the steps outlined in the first two levels, analyzes her situation from a new perspective, refusing to let her previous history contaminate her observations. Notice the difference between her present thinking and her previous interpretations based on mind traps. At last she has a chance of resolving her problems.

"I notice John gets angry when I start blaming him for my problems. I got up late and I knew there was no way I'd have time to get dressed, make breakfast, and still reach the train on time. I wanted John to help out with breakfast—without my having to ask him. When that didn't happen, I cranked up my old song and dance about feeling unsupported, about how nobody loves me. Burning the bagels made it worse. Then I started to hassle him about hurrying up, throwing in a few comments about how much work I have to do in the morning, just to make him feel guilty. What a mess! No wonder he snapped at me. Of course he's going to blow his top if I make him feel bad about himself! I guess I've gotten into the habit of doing that to him. I've got to learn how to ask for help—not beat around the bush. I can't expect John to be a mind reader."

SUGGESTIONS FOR THE READER
CAUTION!!!

The most common disaster in applying this system is in thinking that you have someone else's number. *Don't analyze other people's traps.* To do so practically guarantees you of falling into Trap 3 and creating a lot of anger. Generally, attempts to analyze other people fail because we don't have enough data. It's easy to get stuck in opinions and projections—thinking that the other person's mental processes are the same as our own. Typically, they're not. *You can only be responsible for your own process.*

Choose three specific incidents like Jennifer's over the next week. Write down the thoughts you have about the incidents and reflect on them. Identify your traps. Remember, you may fall into any trap, in any order. Don't try to order your thoughts by traps. Just number the thoughts as they come back to you, taking care to distinguish between the literal conversation you're having with yourself and your hidden agenda, the root cause of your suffering. Although it may seem painful at first, the real pain is in remaining unaware. Only awareness can open you to the range of choice necessary for freedom.

As you apply the exercise to your thoughts throughout the day, you may find your mind returning again and again to certain favorite traps. I mentioned that one of my own favorites is Trap 3, blame—I like to be right. Now here's the good part. That was true twenty years ago, when I wrote the first edition of this book. It's no longer true today, because I've maintained an ongoing commitment to mending my mind that has shifted me toward inquiry as a way to become wiser and to suffer less.

As you make the shift to inquiry, you may find that positive statements can be useful in helping you to let go of mind traps. When I began this journey, noticing that I'd fallen into Trap 3, it helped to ask, "Would I rather be right or would I rather be happy?" The question kept my awareness focused and lessened the conditioned pull of my mind. I've provided a list of various such questions and statements you might use for each of the traps, but it's most helpful to develop your own affirmations. They're antidotes to mindless thinking patterns, and the more meaning you invest in such an affirmation, the greater its power to restore you to equilibrium.

- I don't know the truth of what's happening and why, but I'm willing to inquire into it. (Use this when you find yourself circling between traps without any resolution.)
- Would I rather be right, or would I rather be happy?
- Is it really worthwhile to think-feel-act this way?
- How can I make this situation creative?
- I'm shoulding on myself again.
- Let go of that banana!
- I could choose peace instead of this. (Also from Gerald Jampolsky.)
- Thy will, not mine, be done.
- How would X (Jesus, Moses, Buddha, Thomas Jefferson, Oprah, your grandmother, or whichever teacher/role model has meaning for you) approach this problem?

Jennifer's step toward awareness and understanding is just that—a first step. There is no magical panacea that instantly ends suffering. All of the real ones involve a commitment to a lifetime of awareness. Identifying mind traps is simply one way of many to encourage awareness. Old ways of thinking exert incredible force on our awareness, distorting reality as it's actually unfolding in the moment. Human beings learn by association and repetition and find it difficult to drain the charge out of old beliefs and habitual patterns of reaction that have a lifetime of voltage in them. Old patterns are like riverbeds. You can build a dam, reeducate the flow of the river, and lead it in a new direction, but an unusually heavy rain can easily overwhelm the dam, leaving the river to rush back to its familiar course.

Begin your analysis of mind traps with the small emotional upsets in your life. By practicing with these, you will gradually increase your strength to resist the conditioned pull of larger dilemmas.

CHAPTER 6

Reframing and Creative Imagination

It's often the frame of reference through which we view the world that creates the meaning of events. The same set of facts can look very different when looked at through someone else's eyes. Celeste was a thirty-two-year-old software engineer who complained of frequent colds, fatigue, and back pain that led to lengthy absences from work. When we met, she'd just changed jobs for the fourth time in three years. According to her, the reason for these job shifts was always that one or more male supervisors hated women and purposefully made things difficult for her. The problem, however, was not so much in the men but in the "glasses" Celeste wore that distorted her view of them.

The cause lay in her upbringing. Celeste's father, who died when she was fourteen, had come from a family of five brothers, where males were revered. As fate would have it, Celeste's father had three daughters. His disappointment grew with each child. This unfortunate man was totally unaccepting of his daughters. As a child, Celeste had many times mumbled the wish that he would die. When he did die, she, like most children, held herself responsible for her father's death. Every time she thought of him, she relived her feelings of rage and frustration coupled with guilt. Superimposing this negative frame of reference on all men, Celeste was unable to relate to men in school and then later at work.

When Celeste first began to address her stress and health concerns, she couldn't see that her problems with men—and work—were in her own mind. As far as she was concerned, she was a liberated feminist who saw men for what they were. This was not true. In order to recover her health, peace of mind, and effectiveness she needed to inquire into her own past history, and then learn to reframe her situation—looking at it in a new and more realistic way.

An Exercise in Reframing

Find yourself a pencil and paper and take a moment on this brainteaser.

• • •

• • •

• • •

It's called the nine-dot puzzle. Here are the rules:

1. Connect all nine dots using *four, straight, continuous lines,* no curves allowed.
2. Your pencil must stay on the paper. In other words, you can't lift it up and make discontinuous lines.

Try this for a few minutes before reading further.

If you haven't found the solution, you're in good company. Here's a hint: *Don't get boxed in by the dots.* Take a good look at the shape your attempted solutions suggest. A square, right? That's exactly the frame of reference that's preventing you from seeing the solution.

Try again for a few minutes before reading further.

If you've found the solution, congratulations! If you haven't found it, see the next page. Actually, very few people solve this riddle, even after the hint. To solve the problem, you have to go beyond the imaginary limitation of the square and think "outside the box." Similarly, Celeste made progress only after she identified her own frame of reference and learned to function outside it.

Richard Bandler and John Grinder, founders of neurolinguistic programming (NLP), a powerful scientific method that helps people reframe meanings, tell the story of a woman who was driving her family crazy by being obsessively neat. She vacuumed the rug constantly and became enormously upset if anyone walked on it. Bandler and Grinder first helped the woman into a relaxed state (the relaxation response), where mental connections would be more flexible and new associations could be made. They then had the woman imagine what her house would be like if there were no one there to mess up the rug. No husband to love, no children to delight her. Just a clean rug. She began to associate a perfect rug with being lonely, and a new frame of reference was born. Once she began to see the situation from this vantage point, she delighted in imagining her loved ones returning and walking over her precious rug!

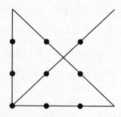

Reframing in Daily Life

All of us have practiced reframing many times, probably without being aware of it. I remember as a high school student babysitting for a six-year-old boy named Mark. As his mother left for the evening, she apologetically told me Mark did poorly with babysitters, often refusing to go to bed. Her advice was that I should let him play in his room until he fell asleep on the floor.

About half an hour after Mark's parents left, I told him that it was bedtime. He barely looked up from the puzzle he was playing with and said angrily, "You're stupid and I hate you. I'm not going to bed and you can't make me."

I was stunned by his hostility, but instead of reacting emotionally, I used a tactic my brother Alan had used on me as a child when I refused to go to bed: making a challenge game out of it. I got Mark's attention pretty easily. "You look pretty slow," I said. "I'll bet you're the slowest kid in your gym class."

That got Mark's attention, and he looked up. Now he was really mad. "No, I'm not," he yelped.

"Yes, you are," I said calmly.

"No, I'm not," he howled.

"Oh, yeah?" I replied. "Prove it. I'll bet you can't even get into your pajamas before I count to thirty."

He was off like a flash. He came back grinning as I hit twenty-eight.

I was unimpressed. "Not bad, but I'm sure you can't possibly wash your hands and face by the count of sixty." He zoomed out, returning shining clean and triumphant in forty-seven seconds.

I was softening up. "Not bad at all. You're faster than I thought. If you can get your clothes folded and jump into bed by the count of forty, then I will read you a story."

After that, Mark and I were fast friends. My little game was reframing, although I didn't realize it then. I got Mark's undivided attention by meeting him in his cantankerous frame of reference and challenging his athletic prowess. The first step in reframing is acknowledging and understanding the other person's viewpoint—or your own. When I shifted Mark's frame of reference toward going to bed, by capitalizing on his own energy, I allowed him to resist me all the way to bed! Using the energy that's tied up in resistance, and channeling it in a new direction, is the mental equivalent of the martial arts, where subtle shifts in balance allow the opponent's energy to be used to your own advantage. In reframing, the opponent is often your own mind-set.

The Art of Reframing

Like all techniques, reframing can be used either to make authentic breakthroughs, or to fool ourselves by shoring up limited points of view. I once had a friend who could reframe any situation in which others accused her of being wrong. It was always *their* jealousy or *their* misperception—never hers. She used reframing to stay stuck rather than to grow. At best, reframing challenges the mind, opening the way to let go of old conditioning so that we can wake up to the moment. The following are different ways to use reframing that can lead to growth if the mind is kept open.

Humor

Humor is the natural response to a sudden shift in frame of reference. Remember the old childhood riddle: What is black and white and red all over? The mind searches in the nine-dot square of color. Of course, the solution isn't in there. The answer, a newspaper, is a member of a totally different set. The sudden shift forces the mind to loosen its grip on "reality" and open up to a new understanding. The physiological result is a delightful symphony of good feelings, and according to recent research those feelings are good for your health. Laughter increases the function of natural killer cells that destroy cancer cells and viruses; increases the production of antibodies; lowers blood pressure and protects against heart attack; reduces food cravings; energizes the body by increasing oxygen in the blood; increases pain tolerance; decreases stress hormones; relaxes muscles; reduces anger and negative emotions; and encourages joy. Furthermore, laughter has no negative side effects.

One of the finest humorists on the planet is my friend Loretta LaRoche. I first met her when some of the members from the original mind/body programs for cancer patients decided to get together and have a monthly humor night. They invited Loretta to come, and she did. The event was recorded, and when I listened to the tape, I couldn't stop laughing. But Loretta was more than funny. She had a genius for positive psychology and reframing, illustrating how bizarre our thinking can be. Here's an example from one of her routines. Do you ever stand in a long line and say something like "Why does this always happen to me?" Loretta's way of questioning that silly frame of reference ("I'm a victim") goes something like this: "Maybe people see you driving into the parking lot and call their friends. She's coming! Get right over there now and stand in line!" Ridiculous, right? That's Loretta's point. Our thinking is often ridiculous. "Life is a joke," she quips, "and you're it."

The problem is that the older we get, the less we laugh. A child of kindergarten age laughs about three hundred times a day. The average adult is a sourpuss by comparison, laughing fewer than twenty times daily. And for some people I know, laughing just once or twice a day would be a bona fide miracle. But if they did, it might reduce their stress levels, create a new frame of reference, and help them let go of mindless worrying.

My son Justin is an inveterate reframer—the sort who puns and jokes a lot. When he was three or four, we were in my parents' home. The sirens of fire trucks and ambulances disturbed the night air and filled my mother with disastrous imaginings that she shared with everyone else. Justin quipped, "Grandma Lilly, don't worry, it's just Siren and Garfunkel." The resultant laughter broke the tense mood and shifted my mother's frame of reference. I still remember that moment whenever I hear a siren.

Steve Maurer also taught me a joke that I'll never forget. Not only is it a great example of reframing, but the reframe itself is also worth remembering. It concerns two great beings, Jesus and Moses, out playing a round of golf. Jesus tees up at a long par-four, 420-yard hole. He sizes up his golf bag and chooses a three iron. Moses shakes his head doubtfully.

"Jesus, it's a long hole. You'll never make it with a three iron; better use a driver."

Jesus smiles and replies, "Arnold Palmer does it." Then he hits the ball with a resounding thwack, and it lands right in the middle of a big water hazard. Moses is feeling forgiving and offers to shag the ball and give his friend another crack at it. So he saunters over to the water hazard and, with great aplomb, parts the waters and picks out the ball. Jesus tees up again, and again he takes the three iron.

Moses laments, "Jesus, you already tried that iron. Believe me, the hole is too long. Here's a driver."

Jesus patiently shakes his head and steps up to the ball. "Arnold Palmer does it," he says. Then he hits it smartly and the ball sails high and short, landing once again in the same hazard. This time he motions Moses to stay put and goes off to shag the ball himself. He approaches the hazard, walks across the water, and picks out the ball. Meanwhile the next foursome has caught up from behind and is looking on, astonished,

"Who does he think he is," says one man. "Jesus Christ?"

"No," says Moses sadly. "Unfortunately, he thinks he's Arnold Palmer."

The reframe to remember is that we're a lot like Jesus in the story. Although our own inner Self is the source of infinite possibility, creativity, and love, we often identify instead with the limitations of the ego.

Affirmation

In the last chapter I discussed using affirmation to neutralize mind traps. The use of affirmation gradually erodes ingrained patterns of thinking, substituting new understandings and a fresh frame of reference. Affirmations can be used not only throughout the day to specifically challenge and counter conditioned thinking, but also at those times of the day when access to the unconscious mind is at its peak. Affirmations help in reprogramming the unconscious. Access to the unconscious is greatest at the edge of sleep, when waking up, and after meditation. You can choose a couple of affirmations to repeat at those times on a daily basis. Just make sure they're framed positively, since the unconscious doesn't process *not*s. For instance, "I will not be angry with my spouse" reminds you on some level that you *are* angry. Instead, affirm "I am becoming more loving, understanding, and compassionate to my wife (or husband) each day." Rather than affirming "I will lose weight," try "I'm getting slimmer each day, enjoying exercise and healthy eating."

Take careful note of your thoughts when you wake up. If you begin the day with negative affirmations—internal moans and groans about all there is to do or the lack of anything, whether time, money, or love—then you've programmed yourself with a mind-set of scarcity. Counteract such thoughts with a positive affirmation of the desired situation. For instance, "I have plenty of energy to do all the things that are important." Affirmations, at their heart, are station breaks for the opposing point of view.

The end of a meditation is the proper time for affirmation. It's also an excellent time for contemplation, when you bring an idea to mind and then just sit with it, noticing what arises. The unconscious is a storehouse of wisdom from past experience that can bring illumination to ideas or problems and help you think of them in an expanded way.

Hypnosis

Most people aren't quite sure what hypnosis is. It's nothing scary—and you won't find yourself clucking like a chicken unless you've decided that you want to learn that art. In reality, hypnosis is nothing more than fixing the attention, as in meditation, so that new frames of reference can be established. Dr. Herbert Benson and others have shown that the induction phase of hypnosis, often just a breathing or relaxation technique, produces the physiology of the relaxation response. The second phase of hypnosis, after a receptive mind-set is brought about by the relaxation response, is that of suggestion. Hypnotic suggestion often involves taking a perception and suggesting a new frame of reference that will fit the facts equally well. It's a reinterpretation of reality. An annoying pain can become an interesting sensation.

Fear can become a cauldron of positive energy to be used to fulfill your dreams.

Many examples of hypnosis occur in everyday life. If you establish rapport with someone, so that her attention is completely with you, she's likely to be open to what you have to say. This is the basis of good communication. It's also the basis of hypnosis and reframing.

Persuasive public speakers are good hypnotists. They use gestures and voice inflections to rivet attention. It's known that once attention is fixed, lowered voice inflections are most easily picked up by the unconscious. Like it or not, hypnosis is part of every human interaction. My earlier story of getting little Mark to bed is a wonderful example of what is best called indirect hypnosis, since there was no formal trance induction, just a fixing of his attention by my challenge to his speed.

Dreams

Dreams are windows into the unconscious. Since sleep is another time when the Judge is out, what comes into consciousness is uncensored. Many people can recall particularly vivid dreams that occur only once or may be repetitive. Even though they don't consciously understand the dream, they often sense that it's important. Understanding such dreams can be a door to awareness and subsequent reframing. Dreams are often an attempt of the unconscious to produce healing. Consider the following example.

As a child, Janine, a woman in her thirties when I met her, had awakened screaming each night for months with the same dream. She remembered it perfectly twenty-five years later. She and her mother were standing by a lake. On the other side stood a child of about her age, alone and crying. Her mother would give Janine a package and tell her to swim across the lake and give it to the other child. It was well known that a huge snake lived in the water. Janine was afraid to go, but her mother was insistent. So each night she'd jump in, and halfway across, the snake would come rearing out of the water. Janine would awaken terrified and screaming.

Janine was able to use the wisdom of the body/mind to reframe the dream and uncover a new meaning. In a session together one day, I invited her to center on her breathing and rerun the dream as if it were happening. In the relaxed state and safe situation, she was able to stay with the action, instead of coming out of it when the snake reared out of the water. In her imagination, she managed to outswim the snake and deliver the package to the child on the other side. It was filled with delightful foods, special toys, golden coins, and a little blue velvet sack marked "Love." She and the child embraced, and Janine felt wonderful. With some reassurance on my part she jumped back into the water, again encountering the snake. This time it appeared more like a dragon, like Puff from the old Peter, Paul, and Mary song. It scooped Janine up on its tail and they frolicked all over the lake. Finally it carried her back to her mother. She embraced Janine, stroking her hair and telling her how scared she had been to make her swim the lake, but that was what her role was. Parents have to help children confront their fears and learn to be free.

This one waking dream helped Janine to reframe her relationship with her mother. She was a critical person whom Janine sometimes accompanied by the added component of revelation. Most research is a synthesis of problem solving and creativity. There's a cartoon I've always loved of two scientists standing in front of a blackboard. One is explaining a long equation to the other. In the middle there's a blank space, and at the far right there is a solution. Pointing to the blank space, one scientist says, "And then a miracle occurs."

How do we get miracles to happen? Whether inspiration is a divine revelation, a recombining of the contents of the unconscious in novel form, or both, there are certain techniques that favor its occurrence.

The absolute requirement for creativity is blindfolding the Judge. The first part of the creative process needs to be free of inhibitions. Later on, when ideas are fully formed, there is plenty of time to scrutinize them.

The letting go produced by meditation or sleep can be used to enhance creativity. Before falling asleep or near the end of meditation, describe the problem to be solved to yourself in clear and simple terms. A question like "Why is everybody mean to me?" is not likely to bring up anything other than your usual ruminations. Be specific. For example, "How can I improve my relationship with X?" If no answer emerges after several days, review the way you're asking yourself the question. Perhaps the question itself is the frame of reference in which you're stuck.

Creative Imagination and Visualization

When the famous psychiatrist Milton Erikson became paralyzed from polio as a teenager, there were no rehabilitation services

grew up resenting because she was so hard to please. But instea
of viewing her mother's criticism and pushiness as devaluing—
she'd done for most of her life—Janine began to reflect on ho
all the pushing had forced her to grow and extend herself. In fi
ture interactions with her mother, she saw her differently ar
was able to let go of her old anger. She no longer responded au
tomatically to her mother's comments by becoming defensiv
and for the first time in her life, they developed a closer relatior
ship. Janine, in dream symbology, was both herself and the chil
on the opposite shore. Her willingness to confront her fear an
swim the distance allowed her to receive the gifts that he
mother had sent. She was both the recipient and the delivere
Although some people can do this kind of dream work alone,
therapist is often required. Jungian therapists in particular mak
significant use of the waking dream.

Creativity

The unconscious mind is a storehouse of wisdom that can I
drawn upon for creativity. Dreams and reveries have long bee
associated with creative breakthroughs.

Creativity requires special conditions. First, you generally ne
some knowledge about a problem. As the imaginative scient
Louis Pasteur commented, chance favors the prepared mind. I
when—even after you're completely prepared—an inspired sc
tion or idea fails to present itself, you can safely assume t
you're stuck in a limited frame of reference. Some time for s
ness or a change of scenery that gets you out of the box often
cedes a breakthrough, a novel recombination of the f

available. For a long time he sat on his front porch, watching the world go by. But instead of pitying himself, he used his paralysis to become an acute observer of the subtleties of posture, voice inflection, and hidden meaning.

One day Erikson's parents went out and left him strapped into a rocking chair. Unfortunately, he was too far from the window. As he sat imagining how he could look out, the chair began to rock slowly. He soon found that the more he thought about getting to the window, the more the rocking increased. Over the course of the afternoon, he refined his imaginings to produce the greatest motion and managed to rock himself over to the window! This experience led him to experiment with the effect of thinking about different motions, until gradually he helped himself to recover from the paralysis. It was his acute powers of observation that later formed the theoretical framework of his extraordinary expertise in medical hypnosis and reframing.

The notion that mental reviews of physical activities actually cause muscle movements is well accepted. Many athletes use such a mental review as part of their training routine. The Soviets, in particular, use creative imagination to give their athletes a competitive edge. The more we imagine any situation, the more deeply etched the neural circuits become.

Take a moment and try this exercise now. First, release your breath with a sigh of relief and then breathe your way back abdominally from three to one. . . . Next, imagine that you are in your kitchen. . . . Go to the refrigerator and look for a big yellow lemon that's inside. Take it out and feel the weight of it in your hand. . . . Notice the round end where the blossom was and the flat end where the stem was. Run your fingers over the pitted, waxy surface. . . . With your fingernail scrape the skin, noticing the spray, smelling the aroma, and feeling the slippery lemon oil between your fingers. . . . Now put the lemon down on the counter and, with a knife, cut the lemon in half. As the juice wells up to the surface, lick it off.

Did you notice any physiological reaction to your imagination? Most people notice that their mouths pucker and that they begin to salivate as if they were actually licking a lemon. The fact is that your body can't tell the difference between what's actually happening and what you're imagining. When you consider all the negative fantasies that run through your mind each day, it's no wonder that your body stores so much tension. Why not purposely substitute positive fantasies by actively guiding your imagination?

Every time you think about something, you are imagining. The details of the process differ from person to person, but everyone has the ability to imagine. When you are fantasizing, whether positively or negatively, what's your experience? Some people's fantasies are best described as a kind of slowed-down form of thinking. Other people are body-centered: They attend to sensations. Others are visually dominant. Still others relate more to fragrance and taste. There is no right or wrong way to imagine. Since you've done it all your life, there's nothing to learn and nothing to fail at. If you still doubt your own imagination, pretend that you've just hired a window washer who asks for a count of the windows in your house to price the job. Close your eyes and count them. Easy, right?

Since the most prevalent stressor is fear and identification with the contents of the mind, creative imagination can be used very effectively to dis-identify with the cares of the mind and enter an experience of pleasure that is absorbing. This activity, by definition, elicits the relaxation response. It's for this reason that many relaxation audio programs begin with a sequence of imagining that you're in a special, comfortable place. You are then instructed to pay attention to the details with each of your senses. In that way you can let go of stressful thoughts by focusing on something pleasant. You'll have the opportunity to try this at the end of the chapter.

Creative imagination is similar to hypnosis. To "get into" it, first you have to let go. The first step, therefore, is to center on breathing or to meditate for a few minutes. In the second step you are mentally suggesting something that's different from your immediate frame of reference. We know that certain "hypnotically talented" people, about 5 percent of the population, can focus so single-mindedly on a suggestion that they can produce exceptional bodily changes. If you touch such a person with a pencil and suggest that it's a hot iron, redness or even blistering may occur. Similarly, if a suggestion of numbness is made, minor surgery can be performed with no other anesthesia. Although most of us are not so "suggestible," we can still be affected quite noticeably, as demonstrated by the lemon exercise.

There's an important difference between the use of creative imagination and meditation. Although imagination is an outgrowth of meditation, the mind is guided into absorption in a directed fantasy. There is a goal. Meditation is not goal-directed; it's more about being in the moment. Like meditation, creative imagination can be used in long blocks of time or for just a few minutes. The last few minutes at the end of meditation, when the unconscious is most receptive, is the ideal time to practice creative imagination.

Here are the steps to follow for a simple exercise. Since each of us resonates to different images, you can modify the script below to suit your own situation and preferences. Follow it mentally or record it with or without music. The dots (. . .) indicate pauses between suggestions to give your mind and body time to absorb them. Music that you find enjoyable can stimulate imagination and add considerable richness to the experience.

Take a deep breath and let it go with a sigh of relief. . . . On each of the next few out breaths, let go a little more, letting yourself sink down and relax. . . . In a moment you can count back from ten to one, continuing to let go a little more with each out breath. You can use your imagination to help you let go. With each breath, you might float a little higher in a hot air balloon, imagining the feeling of the gently swaying basket. Or you might enjoy lying on a beach, at the tide line, imagining the waves washing over you gently on the in breath and receding, taking with them any tension or disease, on the out breath. . . . Perhaps some other image comes to mind. . . . So count back from ten to one in the way that suits you best. . . .

Now imagine a beautiful sunlit day in a peaceful place. It may be someplace you know or someplace that comes to mind now. . . . Let your senses fill in the details. What is the earth like under your feet? . . . Imagine how the sun feels, soak up the warm glow, and take it deep inside, letting it energize and balance every cell. . . . How does the breeze feel? . . . What are the colors like? Imagine all the things that make the scene beautiful. Are there sounds? Birds or wind or surf? Enjoy yourself there. . . .

Now find a comfortable spot and settle into it. . . . Imagine your breathing as a stream of warm, loving energy. Direct that loving feeling into your head . . . your neck . . . your shoulders. . . . Breathe that feeling of warmth into your arms and hands. . . . Fill your heart with love and let the feeling suffuse your entire torso. . . . Breathe love into your belly . . . your pelvis. . . . Feel it traveling down your legs . . . right to the bottoms of your feet.

Now imagine yourself looking healthy and peaceful. The sunlight is shining very brightly. As you breathe in, let your breath enter your body like a sunbeam through the top of your head. With each in breath, allow the light to grow brighter and brighter. The light is peaceful and loving. Rest in that love. . . . Now sit quietly in meditation for a few minutes to allow your unconscious mind to absorb your experience, and then, whenever you're ready, come back and open your eyes.

SUGGESTIONS FOR THE READER

1. Continue to practice affirmation. When you awaken in the morning, notice what you're saying to yourself. If it's a negative train of thought, substitute a positive affirmation for it. Throughout the day continue to check into your thinking. Avoid helplessness by taking action on things whenever you can and letting go or reframing when appropriate.

2. Practice looking for reframes. How can you see a situation differently so that it becomes a learning experience rather than an exercise in blame or guilt? A big reframe is to love what you have instead of lamenting over what you don't. Research on gratitude shows that spending just a few

minutes a day writing down things that you're grateful for reduces anxiety and depression, lessens stress-related physical symptoms, improves immune function, and encourages optimistic thinking.

3. Try creative imagination. You might use it for problem solving, imagining a "wise person" within yourself or asking clear and concise questions of your unconscious before bed or during meditation.

4. Use the script at the end of the chapter for a longer exercise in imagination, or try one of my many audio programs, listed in the resource section at the end of this book.

CHAPTER 7

Healing the Emotions

Peg is a delightful, warm, outgoing young woman who is married to an adoring husband and has two young sons. Peg wanted to try mind/body techniques for severe migraine headaches that often lasted for up to four days. When we first met, she described herself as a "supermom" and "superwife." She began to cry as she talked about the previous weekend, when her husband's two sisters and their families had arrived at her home, with no notice, for a day at the pool. Although extremely angry, she had smiled and acted the perfect hostess. When everyone left, she collapsed into bed with a sick headache but was unable to sleep until 3 a.m.

Peg had no trouble telling me how angry she was, but she couldn't seem to tell her family. And although she focused her fury on her sisters-in-law, the real source of her anger—her parents—took a while to surface. She explained that she usually held in her emotions, but they occasionally erupted and then she'd yell at her husband or children. Whenever that happened, they blamed her for being overemotional and out of control. Peg would then be hurt and angry and end up feeling guilty that she'd acted so childishly. With little awareness of what she was feeling and why, Peg was like a time bomb. When the pressure got too intense, she exploded into a rage or experienced a migraine. In Peg's mind everything was either the fault of other people's selfishness or her own fault for being less than perfect. She was caught in three mind traps: personal put downs, societal *should*s, and blame. In childhood she'd learned the role of perfect daughter—safekeeper of the family feelings. She did what she was told, keeping everyone happy. But in the process she never learned what was needed for her own happiness and balance. At thirty-four she hadn't learned how to say no. In her own words, Peg was a doormat.

Emotional Mind Traps

In 1975, Harvard psychologist and neuroscientist Howard Gardner realized that understanding how "smart" a person was based on IQ testing was much too limited an idea. He began to formulate a widely accepted theory of multiple intelligences: Some people are good with words—they have linguistic intelligence. Others excel at logic and mathematics. Some have musical intelligence, and others are good at reading people—they have interpersonal intelligence. Some people excel at self-understanding or intrapersonal intelligence, and others have a profound understanding of the natural world. Peg, for example, had a master's degree in chemistry and a very high IQ. She'd also lived on a ranch in Wyoming for many years and felt a deep kinship with the natural world. On the other hand, her self-understanding—

and her social intelligence in terms of interacting harmoniously with others—was low.

In 1990, two academic psychologists, Peter Salovey and John Mayer, defined emotional intelligence—which is similar to Gardner's intrapersonal and interpersonal intelligences—as understanding how other people's emotions work and being able to control one's own. In 1995, psychologist Daniel Goleman popularized the idea of emotional intelligence (EI), in a delightful and very readable book based on fascinating research findings. His book *Emotional Intelligence* is an excellent source of understanding how emotional skills affect our relationships and our health, and how effective we are in the world.

Goleman's basic definition of EI centers on the capacity to monitor one's own and others' emotions, to discriminate among them, and to use the resulting information to guide one's thinking and actions. His definition expands to encompass optimism, conscientiousness, motivation, empathy, and social competence. It has been widely accepted in business settings, since a variety of studies indicate that EI (and the competencies that comprise it) is a very important indicator of success. There is a wealth of information available on emotional intelligence—and how to cultivate it and to transform negative emotions—including the book *Emotional Alchemy* by Goleman's wife, Tara Bennett-Goleman.

Understanding the kinds of coping styles that reduce your emotional intelligence is a good start in more consciously cultivating this form of intelligence. What follows are the two most basic styles that, in my experience, stand in the way of emotional intelligence.

Bottling Up Emotions

A friend of mine showed me a journal that his father had kept while doing relief work abroad. Whereas it described people, scenery, meals, clothing, and daily responsibilities, there wasn't a single mention of the writer's own emotional state or that of other people. It felt like reading something that had been written by a space traveler from another galaxy—perhaps the famous Dr. Spock from *Star Trek,* who was portrayed as totally without emotions or emotional understanding. Emotions were simply lacking in his corner of the universe—as they are for some people right here on planet Earth. In 1973, psychiatrist Peter Sifneos coined the word *alexithymia*— from the Greek, meaning "without words for emotions." About 85 percent of individuals with the spectrum of autistic disorders suffer from this deficit, which is likely neurological in nature.

The inability to express emotions in people who don't have alexithymia, but are still out of touch with their feelings, has been linked with a number of illnesses, from back pain to headache. Emotional repression and the avoidance of conflict were once thought to be a predisposing factor for cancer, and the label used was type C personality. These are the ever-popular "nice" people, who are kind and helpful and almost never make a ruckus about asserting their own needs. Like Peg, they tend to be doormats. This type of emotional style was originally defined by psychologist Lydia Temoshok as a "chronically blocked expression of needs and feeling" and the belief that it's "useless to express one's needs."

Although type C personality didn't pan out to be a strong risk factor for developing cancer, it is important in understanding coping styles. First of all, it leads to helplessness and pessimism, which are linked both to poor health and to the development of depression. A study of women newly diagnosed with breast cancer found that those who denied the negative emotions that typically accompany diagnosis were actually more emotionally distressed (they reported more fatigue and depression) than those who could express their feelings. Since the tension behind the emotion—and the message it's sending—can't be received and dissipated either by talking about it or taking some action if you can't experience it, this kind of pent-up energy is often *somatized*, that is, expressed through the body.

"Do you sweat the small stuff, see the glass as half empty, have trouble making friends, and keep your feelings bottled up inside? That combination could be particularly hard on your heart." So began the August 2005 issue of the *Harvard Heart Letter*. The report concerned a Dutch study of "type D" behavior, which was explained above. The *D* stands for distressed, and only time will tell whether this symptom's relationship to heart disease is as robust as early studies indicate. Nonetheless, the initial indications look strong. The Dutch team, lead by psychologist Johan Denollet, completed a prospective study of 286 men and women who had enrolled in a cardiac rehabilitation program. Psychological testing revealed that almost one-third fit the type D profile. After eight years, 27 percent of the type D's had died—mostly due to heart attack or stroke—compared to only 7 percent of the others.

The most common form of bottling up emotions is called denial. It's an unconscious form of protection from painful circumstances and emotions. When something is emotionally painful, rather than coping with it, one uses denial as an unconscious way of avoiding it. I'm an alcoholic? No way. My husband is an alcoholic? No way. My kid is on drugs? No way. But denial is much more prevalent than just in families experiencing substance abuse. It's common to entire societies. Why was global warming denied until it reached a stage of almost no return? Why do we persist in wars and protect ourselves emotionally by calling the soldiers who get wounded, maimed, killed, or traumatized "troops" and largely ignoring civilian casualties? The tendency to repress or deny painful emotions is human. We want to be comfortable and happy. But the price incurred can be high in both personal and global pain. Learning to tune into emotions and acknowledge what we're feeling—Is it sadness, anger, anxiety, compassion, joy, love, shame, guilt, delight, rage, despair, disappointment, elation, hope, fear, bliss, and so on?— is the cornerstone both of emotional literacy and of the kind of transformational coping that minding the body and mending the mind is all about.

Acting Out Emotions

In this trap, which is the opposite of bottling emotions up, you become completely identified with an emotion and can't seem to help acting it out—often to the detriment of others and yourself. Rather than *having* an emotion, you *become* the emotion. Instead of repressing it, you express it inappropriately. This is a particularly dangerous state because it can escalate to complete loss of control. Abuse and other violence are all too often the result. Discrimination becomes clouded, and more primitive impulses prevail. Countries go to war. An enraged man kills his wife. A student shoots his teacher or his classmates. A mother shakes her baby and he's permanently brain-damaged. A crazed driver goes berserk and creates a twenty-car pileup.

One summer my family and I were out fishing on the ocean. A dozen or so boats were gathered around a school of bluefish. Suddenly a speed boat came bearing down on us at incredible speed. There was no time to move out of its way. Fishing lines were snapped as stunned observers looked on. Several boats, including ours, were swamped, and we were soaked. Rocked violently by the wake, and looking disbelievingly after the rogue craft, we saw its name proudly emblazoned on the stern— RAGE.

But you don't have to be a rage-a-holic to qualify as an emotional dumper who acts out feelings inappropriately. Some of us can't help spreading doom and gloom to everyone we meet. We're our own toxic waste dumps. Dumping may lead to relief in the moment, but it makes the people around us feel much worse. If you're scared and stressed—maybe your job or your marriage are on the line—emotional literacy means finding the appropriate circumstances for venting your emotions. Asking someone if he's willing to listen before you blurt out your distress, making sure that the person who is listening is appropriate—a friend who's a peer rather than a child or an employee, for example—is an important aspect of airing emotions. When emotions get so strong that they're hard to contain, visiting a therapist is the wisest course of action. A skilled therapist can often help you understand where the emotions are coming from, why they're occurring right now, and what positive message for growth or adaptation they contain. A therapist can also help you inquire into what you need most—insight or a divorce; a job change or exercise; medication, meditation, or an assertiveness-training class.

A Healthy Attitude Toward Emotions

Just as bottling up emotions or acting them out reduces emotional intelligence, I've found that certain attitudes increase the ability to use them constructively in the quest to be compassionate, balanced, and skillful human beings.

1. *It's natural and human to experience emotions.* What is a human interest story without pain and anger, love and joy? Emotions are the very stuff of life. Welcoming them—without acting them out—is another lesson in surrendering to what is. If you're angry, there's nothing to be gained by pretending that you aren't. Taking some time out—by yourself, with a friend, or with a therapist—can help you understand what the anger is all about. In general, anger is a clarifying emotion. It occurs when your boundaries have been invaded in some way. If they have, anger gives you the energy to take action and restore order and balance in your life. But as we've seen, anger can also be a projection from your past rather than something that's true in the present. Does that boss make you mad because he reminds you of your dad? Is your wife really that controlling, or are you reacting to the way your mother treated you as a child? Emotions are powerful

teachers when you're willing to stay present to, and inquire into, what they have to tell you.

2. *You are entitled to feel whatever you are feeling, whether or not the emotion is "justified."* Neither you nor anyone else has the right to tell you that you shouldn't feel the way you do. It's only through understanding why we feel as we do that we can develop self-understanding and empathy toward others—the intrapersonal and interpersonal forms of intelligence that Howard Gardner identified. When someone takes your remark or behavior the wrong way and feels hurt or betrayed, there's no point in telling that person he or she is wrong. It's disrespectful. If both parties are willing to accept the feeling instead, and are willing to inquire honestly into what caused it, authentic understanding can emerge. In this way a difficult situation can often be transformed into an epiphany of trust, relief, and insight.

3. *Negative emotions create a particularly rich opportunity to enhance self-understanding.* Only by coming to terms with our reactions to ourselves, to situations, and to other people can we heal the residue from the past and experience peace of mind. The positive emotions—love, joy, confidence, peace—are expressions of the Self, our true nature. They're always present and have an opportunity for expression when we free them by learning the art of emotional balance. But the so-called negative emotions—fear, anger, disappointment, guilt, hatred, and the like—can also be positive when they lead to greater understanding, healing, and empathy. Lots of people are angry at their parents, for

example. Yet, for the most part, our parents did the best they could with whatever hand they were dealt. When your anger at your parents becomes an occasion for insight, their behavior might not change—but you can finally let go of wishing that they were different and accept them for who they are.

The Myth of Negative Emotions

Negative emotions are not bad. They're human. Much of the time they are situationally appropriate. When someone you love dies, there is a time of sadness, grief, and mourning that's a human response to losing what is infinitely precious. If you don't allow yourself to experience the pain, it will crop up in other ways, and the wound of your loss won't heal. If you get sick, the most natural response is to feel sad or depressed at what you've lost, anxious about the future, and perhaps angry or frustrated. Although you don't have to stay stuck in those feelings, that's where most people start. The natural reaction to hurt is anger. If you don't express it, how can you learn from it, both for yourself and in order to become more empathetic and emotionally intelligent concerning other people's experiences?

Helplessness, you may remember from the first chapter, is associated with illnesses as diverse as ulcers, heart disease, and even cancer (at least in rodents). Helplessness is an attitude of powerlessness, of victimization. So when a feisty patient shows up distressed or furious over his or her illness or some interaction with a physician, a spouse, or the traffic and then laments that such distress will lead to a recurrence of the disease, I point out that just the opposite is true. It's hiding feelings, believing that you have no right to experience them, and therefore feeling helpless that lead to a more dangerous emotional state and, at least in some cases, to a worse medical outcome. The late psychiatrist Elisabeth Kübler-Ross had a fine understanding of emotions. She counseled people to feel them without "marinating" in them. Anger can provide clarity. But if we hold onto it and become hostile, we pay a high price in terms of interpersonal relationships, peace of mind, and cardiac health.

The only truly negative emotions are emotions that you won't allow yourself or someone else to experience. Negative emotions won't harm you if you express them appropriately and then let them go, as we'll discuss. Bottling them up or acting them out is far worse.

Restoring Balance to the Emotions

Before you can adjust your emotional balance, you have to understand your current emotional style. Do you deny, minimize, or overreact? Sometimes we do fine with some emotions but don't know how to handle others. People's emotional styles can be very different. Each of us comes from a family and from a very different set of life circumstances that have left a unique emotional imprint on us. In some families it's okay to be angry but not sad. In others it's okay to be helpless but not angry. In some families only positive emotions are allowed.

Men, in general, are less accustomed to recognizing their emotional states than are women, since in many families males are rewarded for hiding their feelings—appearing strong and imperturbable. Although there are many cases where this kind of conditioning is reversed, many of my married students tell a similar story about the difference in male/female emotional styles.

The man complains that his wife is overemotional. The woman complains that her husband is too rational, insensitive to her emotions and his own. She says, "I'm feeling sad; my friend Linda and I had a big fight." Instead of comforting her and validating her right to feel sad, her husband prepares the intellectual equivalent of a legal brief, listing the reasons she should think differently and trying to figure out who's to blame. She ends up thinking her husband doesn't care about her because he glossed over her emotional needs and went intellectual on her. He ends up thinking that she's hysterical and unreasonable when his attempts to solve her problem rationally end up making her feel worse.

Any intimate relationship requires an awareness of our own emotional style and that of the other person. It doesn't mean that both people have to have the same style, only that they have to respect the other person's style. If the husband in the above example is aware that his wife experiences her emotions strongly and that it's okay for her to be that way, he can avoid the fight. If he starts the interaction by reflecting back her sense of upset and saying something like "Gee, honey, it looks like you really feel bad about this fight" and then gives her a hug, she'll feel supported and understood. That gives her emotions a chance to dissipate to the point where her intellect can actually be a help in coming to a better understanding of her situation.

At that point she might benefit from his rational perspective. She might also be open to hearing his viewpoint, since the validity of her emotions has first been supported. On the other hand, if he's having a bad day himself and can't relate to her emotions, her awareness of his style can prevent misunderstanding. Instead of blaming him for being insensitive, she can remember that he's just more rationally oriented and going through his own tribulations at this moment. He's okay. She's okay. They're just different. Simply because he can't relate to her problem right now doesn't mean he doesn't love her and support her. This understanding can save her from escalating the mismatch in emotional styles into a fight. Furthermore, she can then appeal to his intellect in letting him know, without blame, that they have just had one of their famous rational-versus-emotional miscommunications. Both learn and no one feels bad.

Understanding Your Emotional Style

Be an objective observer this week. When an upsetting situation occurs, in addition to identifying your mind traps, identify how you're relating to the disturbance emotionally. You may also want to try the following exercise in observing your emotions.

Ever thought back on something that happened and then re-experienced the feelings associated with it? For years I was burdened by the memory of an event that had occurred when I was a teenager. I'd gone to a party that got out of hand and the police were called to break it up. No one was arrested, but a friend of mine told her mother what had happened, and in turn that woman told my parents—who went ballistic. For years afterward, the memory of that party made me feel ashamed. When I thought about it, my posture would change, my voice would become low, and I would become agitated, anxious, and miserable.

That's the power of the conditioned mind. This exercise is designed to help you deal with your mind and the repetitive emotions it can generate.

Part 1: Awareness of Negative Emotions

Get a pencil and paper. Write down two or three memories associated with anger. Fill in as much detail as you can, including what happened and exactly what was said or done. Notice how the memories make you feel, and most important, *locate those feelings in your body*. For instance, some people experience anger as a knot in the stomach, others as a burning sensation in the heart and the throat, and still others as extreme muscle tension or as other sensations. Record your own reactions. Did the memory of anger bring up other emotions like sadness? How do those feel? Record the following:

- The "memory" emotion. In this case, anger.
- The physical feelings associated with the memory.
- Any other emotions that the memory triggered and their associated bodily feelings.

Repeat the exercise with fear, guilt, shame, sadness, and any other negative emotion you wish to—and feel able to—explore. If the emotions that come up feel too strong or uncomfortable, discontinue the exercise and be sure to get professional help.

Part 2: Positive Emotions

Repeat the exercise for love, confidence, joy, peace, or any other positive state. For confidence, write down memories of things you accomplished that made you feel good. They needn't be accomplishments that other people necessarily appreciated. For instance, I can remember the moment I learned to read. First came the struggle of telling an *a* from an *o* and a *p* from a *q*. Then, while I was riding in the car one day, suddenly the letters of a sign clicked into a recognizable unity—STOP. What a high!

People often notice that they can readily reexperience some emotions but not others. The ones that can't be retrieved can be powerful clues to things that you're denying or minimizing. It's the rare person who has really mastered anger, for example, and learned forgiveness. Denial is the more likely explanation. Take note of which emotions came easily and which were unavailable. What did you *do* with the emotion? Did you express it and learn from it, or did you overexpress, deny, or minimize it? Can you think of why that might be? How did people deal with that emotion in your family when you were growing up?

You may or may not be able to get insight into your early conditioning from the exercise. It always helps to share the results with someone who knows you well and may be aware of certain things about your emotional style that you can't see. Furthermore, some people relate to such an exercise more easily than others. Just because you may not feel emotions strongly in this exercise doesn't mean that you're a denier. Ask yourself whether your experience in the exercise coincides with real-life reactions.

Tuning into the body can teach you a lot about what you are feeling. Positive emotions create bodily sensations of openness and expansiveness. They invite the world in. The body feels relaxed, even though some emotions such as joy are very energizing. In contrast, negative emotions create a tight, contracted feeling. Everything pulls inward. The world is pushed away. *Positive feelings invite intimacy and engagement. Negative feelings invite isolation and alienation.*

You may recall that engagement, as opposed to alienation, is an aspect of commitment—one of the three attitudes of stress hardiness. I'm not promising that the skill of engagement is easy to develop, only that it's possible and very desirable. At the emotional balance point, the ego takes a backseat to a curious, moment-to-moment awareness of what is really happening. Egoic wants and fears may still remain, but they're less likely to run the show. Instead, you learn to observe your emotional state with interest and respect. Without judging whether you're good or bad, you can then use your intellect to discern what your feelings reveal about your life. Does anger mean that you have to take a particular action, or is an attitudinal shift required instead? What's to be learned from your fear? Why do you feel helpless and scared in the face of some one's anger?

One of the most important levels of emotional awareness concerns your thoughts themselves. Are the things that you tell yourself—which create and sustain your emotions—really true? If something difficult happens and your explanatory style (the way you explain it) is personal, pervasive, and permanent ("It's my own fault, I mess up everything I do, and it's the story of my life"), as Dr. Martin Seligman describes, you are thinking like a helpless pessimist. Refuting the thoughts that sustain this mind-set is an important component of what Seligman calls learned optimism. For example, you're feeling scared because some one is angry with you (this was Peg's problem). You explain your emotion by saying something like "It's my fault for telling him X. I should have told him Y." Is that really true? Aren't there some people who would have responded entirely differently to what you said? Is it really all your own fault? Are you the final determinant of the other person's experience? When you begin to realize that the distressing stories you tell yourself aren't really true, then you can let them go more easily or tell yourself more empowering stories!

Learning from Emotions

By taking the stance of the observer—the Witness, who notices without judgment—you can gradually learn to experience emotions without becoming overwhelmed by them. When you notice an upset feeling, for example, zoom in with awareness. Where do you feel it in your body? This is an important step. Perhaps what seems at first like anger is more strongly experienced as hurt. *Give the emotion a name.* What are you really feeling? Then reflect on why you're experiencing it. Keep an eye out for your ego, which will trot out all its mind traps to ensure that you or someone else gets the blame or the praise. The idea is not to end the analysis by finding a culprit but by understanding why you react the way you do, regardless of what happened to provoke the emotion and whether there's justification for feeling it. The truth is that anger doesn't have to be justified for it to be okay to feel angry. All emotions are okay. Without them we wouldn't learn much about ourselves or others.

Once you've named the emotion and reflected on where it came from, then you make an informed choice about whether or not a specific action is required. If it's not important, perhaps you can let it go.

John was a fifty-year-old businessman who had had a heart attack. His brand-new Mercedes had got dented in the hospital garage as he was looking for a parking space. When he arrived in my office for an appointment, he reported that he felt anger constricting his chest. The pounding heart and the shortness of breath that accompanied his anger scared him, and he decided that it wasn't worth being angry over a dent. His heart was more important. He took a breath, let go with a sigh of relief, and on the next several out breaths reminded himself to relax further by using the spontaneous mantra "I can choose peace," "I can choose peace."

When you're temporarily overwhelmed by an emotion, breathe and drop back into the position of the observer—the Witness aspect of the Self that notices without judging. This makes a world of difference in your ability to discriminate whether you can let go or whether some action or attitudinal change is required. Witness consciousness also puts you back in control of your feelings. In a rage the intellect is clouded. You're not a person who is angry, you *are* anger. Remember the story of the boat named RAGE?

Regrets and Resentments

After directing the Mind/Body Programs for several years, I began to notice that some people had greater difficulty healing than others. They lived more in the past than the present, bound by sturdy ropes of regret and resentment. When we blame ourselves, regretting some aspect of our lives or who we are, guilt, shame, and disappointment can take over. When we hold onto blaming someone else, resentment and hostility grow. Damage that may have once been real thus persists long after the situation has passed. Some of us are still nursing grudges against people who have been dead for years—including parts of ourselves that have long since changed and ceased to exist.

When you think of a person you still resent, you begin to notice the physical effects. The heart speeds up, the stomach churns, and the muscles tense. The person you're burning up over, in the meantime, is going about her business unaffected. This simple truth crops up in aphorisms and stories from all cultures. The Buddha compared holding onto anger to grasping a hot coal with the intent of throwing it at someone else. You, of course, are the one who gets burned. Dr. Herbert Benson compares anger and hatred to a feast, until you realize that you're the main course! A modern meditation teacher, Swami Chidvilasananda, likens holding onto anger to burning down your house in order to get rid of a rat.

Guilt is a special case of anger turned inward. The rat you're burning down your house to exorcise is none other than yourself. Again, there's nothing wrong with guilt that's dealt with at the time it occurs. It's a message from our conscience that we might have done better to make some other choice—to do something differently. The problem comes when we get the message but can't let go of the messenger. This problem is so prevalent, and so toxic, that I wrote an entire book about it called *Guilt Is the Teacher, Love Is the Lesson*.

Since guilt makes us feel bad, it often spawns spin-off reactions. Let's say that you have good intentions about visiting a sick aunt in a nursing home. You're busy and time passes. Each time you call her on the phone, she asks when you will come. Pretty soon you're too embarrassed to call her. Finally you begin to resent her for making you feel bad. Once the moment passes for dealing with an emotion simply—either telling the aunt that, regrettably, you can't make it or simply making the time—the hole gets progressively deeper.

Letting Go of Resentment and Guilt

Most of us are carrying around a lot of unnecessary baggage full of guilt and resentment. Even when we're not immediately in touch with it, it affects our behavior nonetheless. I can guarantee you that the owner of the boat named RAGE had a gunnysack full of leftover resentments. The anger spilled out in his aggressive disregard of other boaters. A person who is angry with himself may likewise aggress on others. Often the people who are most critical of other people's behavior are those who are most critical of themselves. Their constant efforts to correct and control those around them add to the burden, since their victims are likely to respond with anger and annoyance, perpetuating the cycle.

Before we can let go of resentment, we have to understand why a person who has hurt us did so. Sometimes people are simply unaware of the consequences of their actions. They're not evil—just ignorant. If you don't confront them with the fruits of their ignorance when they hurt you, however, then the opportunity for them to learn may be lost. They're ignorant, but you end up holding onto the resentment. That's not so smart either. Other times people who act hurtfully have themselves been hurt. Most prison inmates, for example, were once abused children. Hurt begets hurt until the cycle becomes conscious and can then be broken by emotionally healthy choices.

A while back I was driving in my car. When I stopped at a red light, I noticed a boy of about ten hanging out the back window of the station wagon in front of me. He caught my eye, curled his upper lip, and gave me the finger. Instead of giving it back, I thought of all the hurt he must have been feeling to express himself in such a hostile manner. So I just looked into his eyes with all the love I could muster. He responded by breaking into a smile and waving at me until his car drove out of sight.

This is an example of an easy exchange—we didn't know each other. It's harder to see how pain affects the behavior of a person who is closer to you. The following two stories are reframes that are helpful in letting go of anger and seeing the reasons behind things that aren't readily apparent.

Reframing Attack as the Need for Love

Robin Casarjian, who lectures widely on forgiveness—and is the founder and director of the Lionheart Foundation, which teaches forgiveness and emotional literacy to prisoners—tells a beautiful story that she heard from the late aikido master Terry Dobson. As the story goes, modified by time and my own retellings, an aikido student was riding in a Japanese subway one hot summer's day. A drunken, foul-mouthed laborer got on the train and promptly cuffed a young woman, sending her sprawling with her baby. Looking around for a fight, he saw only an old man, an elderly couple, and the young aikido student. Fighting is a last resort in aikido, but it seemed that it was the only recourse in order to protect others.

The student and the drunken laborer squared off to fight. The student knew that the drunk was no match for him. But suddenly the little old man tugged on the laborer's clothes, saying he noticed the laborer's enjoyment of drinking. The laborer swore at the old man, who persisted, remarking how he and his wife sipped a bottle of saki each night in their garden as they watched the slow recovery of a little peach tree injured in a storm. The drunk was so astonished that the old man dared talk to him that he began to listen. When the old man asked the drunk whether he had a wife to share saki with, the drunk began to cry, explaining that his own wife had died in childbirth the year before. In his grief he'd lost his job and taken to drink. Soon the drunk was resting his head on the frail shoulders of the old man. The old man stroked the drunk's hair and listened with great compassion to his sorrows. The student, who watched this entire scene unfold, understood that he'd seen a true master of aikido at work.

We're told from childhood not to judge another person until we have walked a mile in his shoes. Nonetheless, it's a hard lesson to take to heart. If we could really relate to the other person's pain, then it would be a lot easier to forgive. Dr. Gerald Jampolsky states the essential reframe very well in his powerful book *Love Is Letting Go of Fear*. In his eyes the attack of another person is best thought of as a cry for help. The attack arises out of the person's own pain, and the only remedy for pain is love and understanding. We can see this most clearly with children. A tired child gets irritable. Sometimes he attacks us, whining, yelling, or even having a tantrum. Do we attack the child back or realize that he just needs a little love and a nap?

Although it's crucial to understand the other person's perspective so that we don't have to take attacks so seriously, I'm not suggesting that you automatically turn the other cheek. At the moment of attack, when anger comes up in you, exercise your discrimination. If a counterattack is the most creative choice, the event most likely to lead you or the other person to a better understanding, then go for it. On the other hand, if the attack is the kind where letting go is the best choice, it helps to reframe the attacker as needing love right at that moment. In all cases, there's no advantage in holding onto anger after its usefulness is gone.

Reframing the Attacker as the Teacher

Another powerful reframe that helps you to let go of resentment is illustrated by the story of a petty tyrant. The late author/anthropologist Carlos Castañeda told the story of an unusually cruel and malicious man who wantonly criticized, dehumanized, and physically mistreated his employee, Don Juan, a Mexican wise man whose teachings form the core of Castañeda's books. Don Juan finally escapes from his tormentor, seeking refuge at the home of his teacher. Amazingly, the teacher sends him back. He assures Don Juan that one of the best ways to cultivate inner freedom is to return to the cruel employer, staying there until no word or deed can draw him out of his center of strength and peacefulness. Everyone, the teacher says, should hope for the grace of a petty tyrant to teach him or her this lesson.

I often think of this story when I encounter petty tyrants in my own life. I try to breathe and let go, centering in the inner Witness, not letting someone else's destructive behavior destroy my own peace of mind. Sometimes I succeed, and other times I fail, but I always try to feel grateful for the lesson. Gratefulness, by the way, is often much easier in retrospect! This story has been one of the most helpful reframes for letting go of resentment, as well as for not getting drawn out into an initial angry reaction.

Finishing Old Business

Letting go of resentments and regrets is a way of freeing ourselves from the past. We can only enjoy the present when all our energy is available in the moment rather than tied up in the threads of unfinished business. When I was in college, I got a letter from an old high school sweetheart named Mark that I'll never forget.

We'd had a rocky relationship. Nothing I did ever seemed to please him. Mark kept professing his love and, like many teenage boys, pressing for sex, but his behavior was at odds with his words. I was angry and hurt when we broke up. I didn't understand what was wrong with me. In the letter, sent four years after we'd last seen each other, Mark apologized for his bad behavior.

He explained that he'd been in love with another girl who was off at boarding school. I was just a stand-in. Instead of enjoying me for who I was, he'd rejected me for not being her. Mark had felt too guilty to tell me what was happening at the time, but it had bothered him for four years. He wanted to say that he was sorry. He wanted to finish his business and let it go. I'll always think well of him for being mature enough to confess his confusion, own his bad behavior, and apologize.

Those of you who are members of Alcoholics Anonymous or other twelve-step programs are already familiar with this principle. One of the steps—the guiding principles through which people can conquer addiction—involves taking a "fearless" inventory of the wrongs you've committed. Then, when appropriate, you apologize to the person or persons involved and do your best to make amends. The little voice inside that berates you for being a bad person can then finally stop its litany of blame.

You can use the same principle to let go of resentment. For example, write a letter telling the person exactly what he or she did and why you're still angry. Some people write such letters without mailing them. It still helps to get the feelings off your chest. Others find that mailing the letter seems the better choice. If you do mail the letter, don't be attached to the results. The other person may not acknowledge the situation or may return new anger. On the other hand, he or she may take the opportunity to apologize to you. In any case, this is your show, your chance to finish your business regardless of how the other person reacts.

During my work with critically ill patients, I've noticed that many have a spontaneous desire to finish old business. For example, Bob, an engineer in his midthirties, was dying from acute leukemia. He had called his ex-wife while in the hospital and requested that she fly from New York to see him. They had a warm and moving afternoon, releasing each other from the blame and guilt that often surround relationships that have ended. He repeated this exercise with his father, his brother, and an old boss. He described the process as casting the stones over the side of his hot air balloon so that he'd be free to float to heaven. Impending death makes the need to finish personal business very pressing. It's too bad that we don't consider living our lives in peace and openness to love to be as pressing a reason for clearing the past.

The Meaning of Forgiveness

Forgiveness is a charged word. Everybody has a different opinion about what it means. To some it's a religious commandment that sounds okay in theory but is difficult to execute in practice. It calls forth images of Jesus dying on the cross, looking compassionately at his tormentors as he prays, "Forgive them, Father, for they know not what they do." Some people relate very positively to this image. To others it seems like abdicating responsibility, becoming a victim.

There's another understanding of forgiveness that is both theoretically sound and practically feasible. It's consistent with any belief system, secular or religious. *Forgiveness means accepting the core of all human beings as the same as yours and giving them the gift of not judging them.* You can be clear about whether or not a person's behavior is acceptable—and take appropriate action—without judging the person. Psychologists

caution parents never to criticize their child, only the child's behaviors. "You are stupid" is a very different statement from "Your
behavior is hurtful." If a person knows that you respect and
value him or her, your comments about behavior are more wel-
come. If you're attacking the person's character, however, no
comment, no matter how perceptive, is likely to be received.
Forgiveness starts with ourselves and extends to others. Accepting that the core of your own being is as precious and wonderful as that of any other person is the greatest gift you can ever
give yourself. Learn to love yourself now, not later. Even if you
haven't lost twenty pounds, finished cleaning the house, become head of your department, or won a Nobel Prize, you're
still a worthwhile human being. Perhaps the most moving personal descriptions of forgiveness and self-acceptance come
from the studies of psychologist Dr. Kenneth Ring. In his book
Heading toward Omega, he writes about the meaning of near-
death experiences to people who have them. (It's notable that a
poll by George Gallup, Jr., indicated that one in twenty adult
Americans has had a near-death experience.)

Ring found that most near-death experiences (NDEs), although variable, have certain commonalities. They begin with a
sensation of indescribable peace and well-being, perceived as
overwhelming joy and happiness. There is no pain or indeed any
awareness of bodily sensation. The person reports floating free of
the body, observing it and the conversations around it in a detached manner. Everything seems very real and natural, not like a
dream or a hallucination. At some point the person becomes aware
of another "reality" and the presence of a Being of Light that radi-
ates total acceptance, compassion, and love. The descriptions of

the light are awe-inspiring. At some point, the Being stimulates a life review that happens almost instantaneously. As one person describes the experience in Ring's book:

> It was not my life that passed in front of me nor was it a three-dimensional caricature of the events in my life. What occurred was every emotion I have ever felt in my life, I felt. And my eyes were showing me the basis of how that emotion affected my life. What my life had done so far to affect other people's lives using the feeling of pure love that was surrounding me as the point of comparison.

When my mother died (the year after this book was first published) my son Justin and I were among the family members keeping the deathbed vigil. Both of us had what near-death researcher Dr. Raymond Moody calls an "empathic death experience." We weren't personally dying, but we went into the light with my mother and had the equivalent of an NDE with some of the same features you just read about.

The experience began with a vision that seemed realer than real. In it, I was both a pregnant mother and the baby being born—one consciousness in two bodies. During the actual birth, that one consciousness moved entirely into the baby, and I came through a dark tunnel and was born into an ineffable, loving light of unconditional love and forgiveness. The light, which was a sentient Being, saw me completely. I was totally transparent to it. Every thought and feeling I'd ever had. Every mistake, every unkindness, every shameful act. And it loved me anyway because it could see *why* I had done those things. Its only concern was my evolution toward greater compassion and happiness. The Being of Light was like the ultimate cheering section.

Scenes of emotional encounters with my mother (we'd had a difficult relationship) followed. It was perfectly clear how we had affected one another, and how our actions—some of which seemed "negative" on the surface—were the source of insight and learning for both of us. The forgiveness and gratitude I felt toward her was overwhelming. When I opened my eyes after the vision subsided, the entire room was filled with light. Nothing seemed solid. Everything was made from an energy that was the same as the Being of Light. My son Justin, who was sitting on the other side of his grandmother's hospital bed, was shedding what seemed to be luminous tears. He looked at me and said in a hushed tone of awe, "The whole room is filled with light. Can you see it, Mom?"

I nodded to him that I could. "It's Grandma's last gift," he continued. "She's holding open the door to eternity so that we can have a glimpse."

Having had this experience, I can personally attest to its transformative nature as a teacher of compassion and forgiveness. Reading similar accounts written by people of all different beliefs, from every possible station in life, I find that the bottom line is always about love, gratitude, and forgiveness. The experience unfolds to reveal a reality where everyone is in a state of absolute compassion for everyone else. Love is the major focus, and in that state everything makes sense. The pain and suffering of life fall into place and judgment drops away; only compelling love and the sense that life is an opportunity for meaning and growth remain. Many people who have a near-death experience are reluctant to go back to life as we know it but understand that they must, that there are still necessary things to be accomplished. Some of the most startling descriptions, however, revolve around what these people consider necessary. Most people report that the accomplishments they had thought most important—in their work, for instance—were of no importance at all. It was the amount of love they shared—expressed in even the smallest ways—that was the most meaningful accomplishment of a lifetime.

People who have near-death experiences often report that they have become much more forgiving of others—they no longer judge. Instead, their primary orientation turns toward compassion. The entire meaning of life is reframed. The challenge to the 95 percent of us who have not had such an experience is clear: *Practice forgiveness by recognizing the perfect inner core (the light, or true Self) of yourself and other people.* If you're not religious, you can think of it as recognizing that the same basic consciousness—whatever its ultimate nature—is present in every person. Only the individuality of our life experiences creates the sense that we're separate. If you're religious, follow the core teaching of compassion that is the mystic core of every great religion.

One of the most active areas of mind/body research is forgiveness. According to research studies, unforgiving people are more stressed, depressed, narcissistic, angry, and paranoid; are less likely to help others; and have more physical symptoms than those who have managed to let go of regrets and resentments. Forgiveness is a potent form of surrender to what is, coupled, perhaps, with gratefulness for what has been learned. The result is that we realize we're nothing and nobody special. Everybody suffers and makes mistakes. Everybody just wants to be happy, and kindness goes a long way to making that so.

SUGGESTIONS FOR THE READER

1. Familiarize yourself with your emotional style. The exercise on observing your emotions should be helpful.
2. Accept your emotions as human. Remember that the only negative emotions are those you push away, since you are then deprived of the learning they can stimulate.
3. Deal with your emotions as they happen; don't store them up. To do this:
   - Give the emotion a name.
   - Take a breath and step back to the position of the observer.
   - Consider why you are feeling the way that you are.
   - Reflect on what you *did* with the emotion. Did you bottle it up, act it out, deny it, or minimize it? Or did you learn from it, allowing it to become a healing force in your life?
   - Choose the most skillful course of action:
      To let go
      To reframe and seek a new understanding
      To take a specific, necessary action
4. Finish your unfinished business. Make a list of the regrets and resentments that you're holding onto. Be fiercely honest with yourself. It's too easy to think you've let something go when you haven't. Do what it takes to finish your business.

Make phone calls; write letters, whether you mail them or not. Apologize and make amends where appropriate for things that you're sorry for. Tell people how you really feel.

5. Practice forgiveness. Let go of your judgments and give yourself and others the gift of being who they are, accepting them for what they are instead of rejecting them for not fitting your expectations.

CHAPTER 8

Sam's Story

Amazing Grace

The radical growth in medical science and technology over the last fifty years has redefined the expectations of both doctors and patients. Before the discovery of antibiotics, it was common for children and young adults to die of infection. Physicians often had little to give other than kindness and support through the natural course of illness—which often ended in death.

By comparison, modern physicians can sometimes work wonders. Now that most acute illness is under control, chronic disease has become the more common problem. And that's where mind/body medicine can make a tremendous difference, supporting the self-healing mechanisms of the body as an adjunct to medical care. Even previously life-threatening illnesses—heart disease, cancer, and AIDS—can often be medically managed for extended periods. Nonetheless, the final outcome for every one of us remains unchanged. Eventually we will all die. Where death was once viewed as a natural part of life, it has now grown remote and is often seen as a failure on the part of medicine to work its miracles. Death has become the enemy.

Many of the patients who have been my most valued teachers through the years were facing death. In the process, they harvested the wisdom of a lifetime, reflecting deeply on what was most meaningful and precious. Curiously, this frame of mind can lead to a depth of wisdom that might have otherwise come more slowly or perhaps not at all. When familiar frames of reference are blotted out by death's long shadow, new insights have the space to emerge. These insights are often spiritual in nature and can be the most unexpected legacy of the loved ones we lose.

Who are we and why are we here? What's the definition of a life well lived? Am I this body or something more? These questions of meaning are what make us quintessentially human. And it is illness and the nearness of death, perhaps more than any other experiences, that put us face to face with them.

This chapter is about what I learned from a young man who died of AIDS in the early 1980s, a time when AIDS was a death sentence for almost everyone who contracted it. There were no drug cocktails that held it at bay, and now—almost a quarter of a century later—I think of those dark times as a terrible harvest of young lives. It was like a war against an invincible, invisible enemy. I met Sam, a young lawyer, in the late winter of 1983. He was hospitalized with *Pneumocytis carinii* pneumonia, an infection often associated with AIDS. In his agitation and sadness, Sam had asked whether anyone in the hospital taught meditation, since he thought it might help him cultivate peace of mind.

Since Sam's story is a very personal one, I'll tell it largely through our evolving conversations. Although I've changed the

outer circumstances and any possible identifying details to protect his confidentiality and that of his family and loved ones, the
words we exchanged—the meditations of our hearts—are true to
the Spirit that passed between us.

As I put on my winter coat and closed the door to my office—
setting out for the unusual "peace of mind" consult he'd requested—I was nervous. Sam was only the second person with
AIDS whom I'd ever met, and I didn't know whether I had anything to offer him. Furthermore, it was beginning to snow and I
had a long drive home through the Boston traffic, and then on
the Southeast Expressway to the quaint oceanside community
where our family lived. I thought of waiting until morning, but
then I put myself in Sam's place. He was very sick, and waiting
for a special kind of help.

When I arrived at Sam's hospital room, the door was plastered
with precaution signs—specific instructions about handling
blood products and bodily excretions. There was a cart contain-
ing sterile gowns, gloves, and face masks outside the door.

The masks were actually for the patient's protection, in case a
staff member had a respiratory infection. Even a cold could prove
fatal to someone in such a weakened condition. As I put on a
gown, I lingered in the preparations, wondering what to expect.
Truth be told, I was scared—not so much about contagion, but
scared that I had nothing to offer some one in such a terrible circumstance. I took a deep breath—said a little prayer—and at last
was ready to go in.

The room was still, brooding in the semidarkness. A nurse,
making soft, reassuring sounds, was moving Sam's intravenous
line. Dozens of cards lined the walls. The late winter sun cast

long shadows across the bed, creating an almost otherworldly feeling. Sam was lying under the covers, pale and shaking, his wet blond hair plastered against his forehead.

I stood in the doorway for a moment, collecting my thoughts. Was he contagious after all? AIDS was still a recent phenomenon, and medical science hadn't yet begun to unravel its secrets. Not even the HIV virus had been isolated and identified as the cause. I thought of Miroslav and our children and wondered if I should even be here. Just then Sam opened his eyes and saw me. He smiled and extended his long, frail hand from under the blankets. "You're Joan Borysenko, aren't you? My father's a doc on staff here, and he mentioned that you might be the one who came."

I moved over to Sam's side—all my doubts dissolved in the openness of this gentle, good man. He thanked me for coming and, in a weak voice, began to tell his story.

Sam had been ill for about six months. At first his physician—and his father—had thought that he had hepatitis. But in spite of bed rest, his condition hadn't improved. When a bad case of thrush, a fungus infection, made his mouth and throat impossibly sore, they began to suspect AIDS—especially since he was gay. At that time AIDS in the United States had been diagnosed almost exclusively in young, gay men. By the time I left hospital practice several years later, we were seeing, among others, young mothers and grandmothers who'd contracted AIDS. It was an equal-opportunity illness transmitted not only sexually but—until the blood supply was finally made safe—even through transfusions of potentially life-saving blood products.

I asked Sam why he'd called for me, intrigued that he wanted a "peace of mind" consult. He'd done his homework with the help of his father, who was an orthopedic surgeon. At first Sam spoke scientifically, about the effect of stress on the immune system and how he'd concluded that the relaxation response might reduce his stress and give his immune system the best chance of recovery. This was Sam's intellectual reason, but his deeper feelings surfaced very quickly as we sat together in the embrace of the gathering shadows. He gripped my hand and began to cry so softly that I barely heard.

Then he continued, "All my life, I've searched for meaning in the things I could accomplish. I became a lawyer—a good one. I felt I was a good son, a good friend, that I worked hard to establish and maintain loving relationships. I've spent my life getting secure, acquiring the things we all think of as important. A house, a car, enough money to do the things I want." He paused to cough and catch his breath, then he propped himself on an elbow and continued in a soft voice. "I've spent a lot of time in therapy, too, trying to understand myself, but somehow all those things don't seem to be enough. Part of me is empty, longing for something. I don't seem to have any peace. That's why I asked for you to come. Do you think that there's really a way to experience peace of mind?"

The room was perfectly still, other than the relentless clicking of the IV machine that delivered the antibiotics that were fighting off Sam's pneumonia. I thought of that long string of zeros—all the things we work so hard to achieve—that have no meaning except when a digit, representing peace of mind, is placed in front of them. And, of course, I thought about my own long search for meaning and peace, wondering if I was up to this challenge. How could I help Sam when I was so often anxious and off-center myself?

In spite of the doubt, words came out of my mouth that riveted us both, coming from a source beyond either one of us: "I can't teach you, because you already have peace inside." I knew the truth of those words with the same absolute certainty that allows you to pick out the face of a loved one in a crowded room.

"But I can remind you of how to experience the peace that you already are," I continued, suffused with a calm presence so palpable and real as to be entirely "beyond understanding." We were both silent, gazing intently at each other. Only a few times in my life had I experienced such a deep connection with another human being. We trusted each other immediately and completely—with an uncanny sense that we'd always known each other. That trust was to take us both beyond our ordinary understanding of life.

I explained the basics of meditation to Sam. He wanted a focus word that reminded him of the inner peace he was searching for. He settled on the breath mantra, *Ham Sah*—"I am that," the peace, the consciousness out of which everything arises and to which everything returns. We had a few minutes of meditation together before the silence was broken by his nurse, who came in to check his vital signs and adjust the IV. She commented on how much better he was looking.

It was getting late, and the last fingers of daylight had long since caressed Sam's tired face. The Boston skyline was breathtaking from his picture window, particularly against the backdrop of the twinkling city lights and the gently falling snow. Sam looked at me with a special, tender smile—a smile that I returned. We made a plan to check back in the following morning before clinic hours began.

I thought of Sam all the way home. How strange life could be. Here I'd just spent an hour with a young man who was fighting a deadly disease, and yet I wasn't depressed. A palpable sense of peace had descended on us both, and it was still with me.

The next day I arrived at the hospital to find Sam much improved. The antibiotics were taking effect and he was sitting up in bed. He'd already done a morning meditation, and he asked the usual questions about the wandering mind. We soon began to talk of Sam's favorite hobby, downhill skiing. His body posture changed, and you could feel the vitality in him as he spoke of how quiet his mind became when he concentrated on the body feelings, the balance and dexterity, that skiing demands. Just remembering the experience of speed and control brought a look of peacefulness to his face. As he brought back that memory, he understood that peacefulness is the constant background of awareness that's reexperienced whenever the mind slows down. It's our essence, our true nature. We sat quietly for a while, both pondering times of peace. Just as I was recalling a long-forgotten childhood memory, Sam's voice roused me from my reverie.

"Can the mind stop during intense fear, do you think? If you're totally riveted in fright, can the experience actually reveal the peacefulness behind it all?" How strange that he'd asked—and yet how perfectly in keeping with what was being revealed. The question related intimately to my early memory that had surfaced.

When I was three or four years old, my father and I were playing in a swimming pool. He was a porpoise and I was a mermaid riding on his back. Suddenly slipping off—scared out of my wits—I sank. Floating upside down near the bottom of the pool, I found myself enjoying how the filtered sunlight danced in the water. The body of a swimmer passed above, setting up undulating currents. The sudden surprise of such an enchanting world completely stopped my mind, and peace overtook fear. Fortunately, my father's strong arms quickly scooped me up before I needed to take another breath.

Sam was shaking his head, quickly making associations between my story and a book his lover, David, had been reading to him, Kenneth Ring's *Heading toward Omega*. Books about near-death experiences were quite popular at that time—in the early 1980s—and became popular again twenty years later. Sam was amazed that although people who'd reported NDEs all had different perceptions, there was still a common thread of experience. "For example," he mused, "in a matter of seconds complex, and highly meaningful, scenes from your life—and your relationship to others—replay. Isn't time perception strange? It's mind-boggling to think that the brain could present so much information in a way that's consciously meaningful in what must be literally seconds."

"Mmm," I mused. "I've thought a lot about that, too. Meditation points up the relativity of time. Sometimes ten minutes seem like an hour, but other times an hour seems to pass in a minute. Einstein said that when you're sitting on a hot stove, two minutes seem like two hours, but when you're in the arms of your beloved, two hours seem like two minutes. Isn't it true?"

We both laughed, and then Sam continued, shifting his position and encircling his legs with his arms so that he could rest his chin on his knees. He was gazing off into space.

"After their life review," he continued, talking about people who've died clinically and then been resuscitated, "people sometimes see a tunnel, which feels very appealing. At the other end of it they emerge into a peaceful, totally accepting light, which seems to know them personally. It loves them just as they are—with total forgiveness and understanding—regardless of what their experience in life has been. It's like your swimming pool memory. They don't get scared, don't get into some rap about what they're missing back at the ranch; they just surrender to the love. It's like a homecoming. At this point, according to what I've read, the experience gets pretty variable. Some people talk about seeing deceased family members, a Being of Light, or different saints and religious figures. Then they have some kind of recognition, or sometimes a clear communication, from the Being of Light or a family member, that it's not time to go yet, and they're transported back through the tunnel and into their bodies."

I sighed, about to tell Sam a story about a scientist I'd met a few months earlier, but I changed my mind. Interrupting wasn't a good idea. He needed to talk about death and make sense of what he'd read and what it meant to him. I prompted him to continue: "What do you think about those accounts, Sam? Do they make any sense to you?"

He nodded. "I think so. I'm not religious, but I am spiritual—and I do believe that we're here for a purpose. On the other hand, I remember reading an article from *Psychology Today* a few years ago that tried to reduce those experiences to some preprogrammed trick of dying brain cells, some way that we could die in peace. Even if that's true, though, it's hard to attribute such a great design—the last video game of the show—to chance. I'd have to believe that such an exceptional program was created by some intelligent, loving force, and then the point becomes moot.

We're talking about God either way, so why invent theories? If some people have actually experienced this, I want to learn more. It certainly challenges my ideas about what death is."

We looked at each other and said in unison, "And what life is." We both giggled in relief. It broke the spell for a moment, and I got up to stretch and examine the magnificent arrangement of anthuriums, shiny red, heart-shaped flowers with a waxy appearance, that rested on a table by Sam's window. I remembered seeing them on a trip to Hawaii, where they grew in great profusion. I'd had an anthurium plant for years as well, and it had actually bloomed from time to time. The resemblance of the blooms to hearts seemed to capture the mood of the moment. Sam and I discussed his brother, who'd sent the arrangement. He had so many good friends and such a supportive family.

"You started to say something a few minutes ago when we were discussing near-death experiences," Sam said. "What was it?"

I had to pause. I rarely ventured into the realm of the spiritual with patients, and it made me uncomfortable. I was a medical scientist and psychologist, not a chaplain. We discussed my feelings and reservations and concluded that the work Sam and I were engaged in together was different from my usual hospital practice. We were both teachers and both learners. It seemed best to see Sam as a friend on my own time, rather than as a patient. That decided, it felt appropriate to continue with my story.

I began to recount a trip to a scientific conference where I'd met a leading immunologist named Dan. The meeting was a seemingly chance occurrence in the hotel coffee shop before the morning sessions began. It was very crowded, and people had begun doubling up at tables. When Dan sat down, we introduced ourselves and said a few words about what we did. When he heard that I had an interest in mind/body interactions and in exploring the mind through psychology and meditation, he became pensive. He then asked permission to tell me a story that had been deeply disturbing to him. Dan still didn't know what to make of it and thought that perhaps I could help.

Several months earlier Dan had been hospitalized with acute abdominal pain, and a number of tests had been ordered. He'd been given a narcotic to ease the pain and apparently had a bad reaction to it. His body got hot and restless. Dan then began to feel strangely energized and had the odd and compelling sensation of rising up to the top of his head and exiting through a hole near the back of his skull. He described the sensation with wide eyes and a sense of wonder.

"I—that is, the thinking, sentient part of me, what I would label as my identity—rose up out of my body. I hovered around the ceiling, looking down on the sweaty body below, as if I were seeing it in the movies. I remember noticing how filthy the top of the moldings were and making a note to tell the nurse later. In the meantime I overheard them discussing my case in the hall. I simply floated through the wall, without even noting it as a barrier, and observed the conversation. I clearly perceived that the internist was preoccupied with family problems and that I wasn't going to get the care I needed from him. I was sure of it. Don't ask me how. I just knew, clearly and absolutely. In that moment I also had a strong impression of what was causing my problem. I was having referred pain from a kidney infection that had nothing to do with my GI tract. At that moment I felt a strong pull back to my body and had the sensation of slipping back in through the back of my skull.

"Then I made the mistake of trying to discuss my experience with the internist. He wanted to put me on tranquilizers. He thought I'd had a hallucination caused by the drug and called the psychiatry department for a consult. Meanwhile I got up, got dressed, kidnapped my chart, and called a cab, leaving the hospital AMA—against medical advice. I had the cab drop me at a hospital across town, where I knew one of the internists on staff. As luck would have it, he was on call when I arrived. I explained my hunch to him, and it proved correct. I didn't explain how I had come to have the hunch, since I don't think most people will believe me."

I'd been listening with rapt attention, wondering why Dan was telling all this to me—a complete stranger. Dr. Bernie Siegel, a former surgeon and early writer on mind/body medicine, explains such apparently serendipitous phenomena with the quip that co-incidence is merely God's way of remaining anonymous. Perhaps so. It seems as though when we become interested in a larger in-telligence—and in our life's purpose—a more meaningful reality reveals itself in little synchronicities and sometimes in miraculous interactions like the ones that Sam and I shared. I asked Dan how he felt about his unusual experience—whether it had changed his ideas about life. He laughed and said, "That's the understatement of the century. There's no way anymore for me to assume that I'm just a body. The body was more like a suit of clothes that I slipped out of at the end of the day. The essential me was independent of the body. Of that much I'm absolutely sure. Beyond that, I don't know what to think, other than I need to know more."

We went on to discuss descriptions from the spiritual literature—Jewish, Sufi (the mystical, inner tradition of Islam), Christian—and the literature on NDEs that paralleled his hospital story. In the twenty-five years since I met Dan I've heard hundreds of similar stories, although many people are still uncomfortable telling them for the same reason Dan was. People might think you're nuts—or at the least label you a credulous New Ager, regardless of the fact that similar experiences have been reported in every culture and religious tradition.

I was feeling a little sheepish about going on for so long, but Sam just looked at me and said something that brought tears to my eyes—something I'll always remember. With great tenderness, he said, "Your children must really love you." My story was meant for his mind, but it had penetrated his heart instead.

There was often a timeless quality to our meetings, as on this occasion. At other times the talk was of immediate problems, of the reality of being so sick. Of all the diseases that I'd seen people cope with, AIDS, in its early days, was the most difficult. Because it was sexually transmitted and began in the gay subculture, it had brought out a parade of fear and prejudice. People who were preoccupied with the idea of a punitive God imagined AIDS to be a divine punishment. Having to cope with such narrow-minded beliefs was an additional burden for AIDS patients then—and it remains so for some even today. Yet even this burden can be a blessing. It can lead to a reevaluation of old beliefs and to authentic inquiry into the perennial questions "Who am I?" and "Why am I here?" When fearful dogma is replaced with faith in a loving Source, then it can birth compassion and make room for peace.

Sam's emotions were quixotic. One moment he'd be lost in an emotional wilderness of fear. The next he'd be blissed out—lifted by a profound sense that even AIDS was part of some larger plan. I remember feeling a powerful identification with what he said. One minute everything made sense; it seemed like grace. The next I would wonder if it wasn't all some sort of delusion.

The fascinating theories of Belgian physicist Ilya Prigogine, who won the Nobel Prize in 1977, became very meaningful to both of us. You probably remember from high school science that the universe is running downhill according to the second law of thermodynamics. In other words, order necessarily degenerates into chaos. You may also remember that living systems oppose this law, since more complex systems are always evolving. Prigogine showed that the stimulus for creating order out of disorder is exactly the opposite of what you might imagine. It's actually throwing a monkey wrench into the works that stimulates the creation of new structures at an atomic level and new meanings at a personal level.

Prigogine's theory of "dissipative structures" states that small perturbations in a system may be damped out, swamped by the status quo, so that no real change is produced. But if the monkey wrench is big enough, if the perturbation is strong enough, the system can't absorb the shock. An opening is created for the whole structure to undergo a startling change, an evolution that Prigogine calls an "escape to a higher order." AIDS is a major perturbation—a potential doorway to the possible—that Sam and I went through together.

After Sam went home, we stayed in touch by phone and met in person from time to time. We saw each other most intensively during his hospitalizations. He developed a serious herpes infection one time. Then he had a second bout of pneumonia. On the last occasion, Sam battled an intestinal infection. He also had a host of other medical problems, not the least of which were the side effects from the drugs he was being given to stimulate immunity. But he was always at the ready to fight for the life he loved more than ever. No matter how long the odds on a treatment, he'd try it. He figured that even if it didn't help him, something of value might be learned for the benefit of others. Nonetheless, he grew progressively weaker. He was hospitalized for the last time in the early spring, just a little more than a year after we'd met. His energy was low, and he was often confused. He was also scared.

Late one Thursday afternoon I stopped in to see him on my way out of the hospital. He looked like a child, huddled in bed, clutching the blankets around him. He started to weep when he saw me, telling me how hard it was, particularly the long nights. Even with the support of a dear friend who stayed with him, his fear was intense. He kept pointing to his heart, talking of a terrible constriction in his chest: "It's like all the fear that I've been holding onto throughout my life is trying to leave all at once. My fear of intimacy, of not being good enough, of everything—I want to let it all go. I hope I can let it all go." He looked at me with such longing. At first I didn't know what to say.

Then I remembered a yantra—a visual focus for meditation—that I'd used for years. It's a square within which is a circle. Inside the circle is a triangle, and at the center is a cross. Variants of this symbol are used by many groups, including Alcoholics Anonymous. It's reminiscent of the sketch drawn by Leonardo da

Vinci—a man standing in the shape of a cross in the center, juxtaposed to the form of that man with legs and arms outstretched like triangles. The man stands within the circle, which, in turn, is enclosed within a square. It is an archetype—a universal symbol of our place in the universe. Without explanation, I drew it for Sam with a magic marker on the back of a paper plate. It was something to focus on when fear overtook him.

He was calmer the next morning. His family was gathering around him, since the end was near, and he invited me to join them. That night I was restless and began to prowl through my house like a cat. I rummaged through my drawers to locate an old medallion in the shape of the yantra. It was in the bottom of an old jewelry box, scratched and pitted with age.

I sat for a long time that night, holding the medallion and wondering how people manage to keep their faith in a world so full of suffering. My own faith seemed to come and go like the tide. It had been strong when I was a child and had faded during adolescence, only to return more strongly than ever when I was a young adult. Then, over the years, it had faded once again and disappeared into a thicket of doubts. It had been at a low point before I met Sam. I was experiencing what the medieval mystic St. John of the Cross might have called a dark night of the soul. I felt alone, any connection to a larger whole eclipsed by the cares of life.

Recalling my spiritual journey as I sat holding the yantra, I said a prayer for Sam and for us all—not knowing whom or what I was praying to, but nonetheless feeling a renewed connection to a meaningful spiritual reality. Finally, I tucked the medallion into my wallet and fell asleep.

The morning dawned clear and crisp. It was one of those sweet, early spring days that make you remember how long the winter is. The air smelled like earth, and purple crocuses were peaking out through the wood chips by the front walk. Spring was Sam's favorite season. I fed the kids, said bye to Miroslav, and set out for the hour-long drive to the hospital—mercifully short because it was a weekend and traffic was light.

The snow tires were still on our old van, and they made a familiar humming noise that was hypnotic and reassuring. Absorbed in Sam's story during the drive, I reviewed how we had helped one another find meaning and purpose. And now, this chapter of life was about to end for both of us. The essence of life is change, of course. We know that theoretically. But death makes it real.

It had been a year of admitting some of my own fears—the first step to healing them. Despite all my accomplishments, I was still deeply insecure. I'd perfected an outer mask of competence so convincing that it was easy to deny what was underneath. Being with Sam had helped me appreciate my own innate goodness. I didn't have to be smart. I just had to be present with an open heart and that was enough. What a precious gift he'd given me. Sam had been a bridge for me, as I had been for him. Despite the fear that was still there for us both, we'd tasted peace individually and together. And we knew what parted the great sea of fear to reveal the peace at its depth. It was love. What a grace that we'd found it in one another in such an unlikely circumstance.

As all these thoughts and feelings overflowed through my heart, the old spiritual "Amazing Grace" welled up inside. I sang it over and over again the rest of the way to the hospital.

Sam's loved ones were in the sunroom at the end of the hall letting him rest. They told me that he was losing ground fast but was still conscious. We all went into his room together, and my heart ached at the sight of him. He looked so small and shrunken, dwarfed by a huge bank of heart-monitoring equipment. A unit of blood slowly dripped into one arm. The contents of several IV bags dripped into the other. He reached out to me as I approached his bed, and I leaned down to give him a hug. Then I remembered the medallion tucked away in my wallet. I wanted it to rest over his heart, but I'd forgotten to bring a chain. One of his friends found some string, and we improvised a necklace. I bent down and gently placed it around his neck. With his eyes closed, Sam reached for the medallion and held it for a moment. Then the most remarkable thing happened. He opened his eyes and smiled, then asked me to sing "Amazing Grace."

I was thunderstruck. It was only my shock that allowed me to overcome the embarrassment of being asked to sing that spiritual in a room full of strangers. As the words poured out, each one took on a world of meaning. When I got to the verse "Through many dangers, toils, and snares I have already come, 'Twas Grace that brought me safe this far, 'Tis Grace shall lead me home," there was a peace inside like nothing I'd ever experienced before. At moments when my faith wavers, I have only to recall that moment. The room was completely silent when I finished, and Sam invited the group to join in a short meditation.

When the meditation was over, Sam did an extraordinary thing. One by one, he called the most meaningful people in his life over to his bedside. Then he just spoke from his heart. He told them how much he loved them; he asked for their forgiveness for whatever pain he might have caused; and he forgave them in the same way. That was amazing grace in action.

When Sam was finished, he lay back to rest, and his lover, David, played tapes of Sam's favorite music. Family and friends came in and out of the room, reminiscing, crying, talking to Sam and one another all afternoon. I was surprised when the strong, sweet voice of Leontyne Price filled the room, singing—what else?—"Amazing Grace." I hadn't known that it was one of Sam's favorite songs.

Toward evening it was time to head home. I kissed Sam goodbye for the last time, and not long after, he died peacefully in his father's arms. The memorial service was scheduled for the following week, when I was in New Orleans on business. It was so very disappointing not to be there.

But I hadn't counted on the mysteries of time and space that open magical doorways wherever love builds bridges between our hearts. I was wandering through the narrow streets of the French Quarter at dusk, thinking of Sam. Turning right on a tiny, almost deserted street, I caught sight of a saxophonist silhouetted in a doorway. He followed me with his gaze, and then—when we'd made contact—he nodded and raised the time-burnished instrument to his lips. Closing his eyes with reverence, he began to play "Amazing Grace." Coincidence or synchronicity? And what is a synchronicity other than a spiritual manifestation of minding the body, and mending the mind?

In the more than twenty years that have passed since Sam and I accompanied one another on this journey of body, mind, and Spirit, I've thought of him countless times. He was part of my inspiration to leave the hospital setting in 1988, so that I could talk about the spiritual dimension of medicine freely. And he was part of my continuing effort to learn more about the immune system, the physiology of meditation, and the ways in which our attitudes toward life affect our health.

But more than anything, Sam taught me that the principles of stress hardiness—where we started together at the beginning of this book—are true. Life is a *challenge*. Everything is always changing, and our only safety is in recognizing that essential fact of life. The only authentic *control* we have lies within us—and our attitudes toward life. Regardless of how positive your thinking is, bad things still happen to good people. You may not get what you want. Real wisdom comes in loving what you get. And all of us will die, regardless of our druthers. The death rate has always been the same: one per person. But it's not so much about when you die as how you live. That's the only real control you'll ever have.

And finally, Sam taught me about *commitment*—about engaging with life in a way that was so deep, and real, and beautiful, that I've never been the same. Does life have a meaning? I think so—just look around you at the magnificent potential of which we're all a part. Do we have a purpose personally—you and I? I think so. But it may not be saving the world. Perhaps it's just being the eyes, and ears, heart and soul, of a Reality so vast and loving that it needs us as its organs of perception and appreciation. Be here now. Love what you have. Celebrate life. That's minding the body and mending the mind. And that is Spirit in action.

EPILOGUE

Putting It All Together:
Twelve Brief Reminders

1. *You cannot always control the external circumstances of your life, but you can control your reactions to them.*
   In trying circumstances, remember your choices:
   a) Reframe the situation as a challenge rather than a threat. Remember that the only constant in life is change itself. In this way you acknowledge and nourish your own inner strength, even as you face doubt and uncertainty. Adversity is the crucible in which the spirit is forged.
   b) Your breath is always with you, serving as the key to self-awareness and remembrance of your choices. In stressful circumstances it's easy to forget that although circumstances change, there is a changeless and peaceful place within you—the inner Self, or Witness, your true nature—that remains capable of observing the constant movies of the mind without becoming identified with them. *You have thoughts, but you're not your thoughts.*

c) Breathe in and let your breath travel all the way out. The next breath comes automatically, and the diaphragm resets. Focus on abdominal breathing, perhaps using an image to help you. The belly expands like a balloon on the in breath and deflates on the out breath; a bird spreads its wings on the in breath and folds them closed on the out breath. Feel the movement of the breath in your belly as you count down, ten to one or five to one, or remember *Ham Sah* ("I am the Self that observes"). The frequent use of such minirelaxation responses throughout the day helps to reinforce your sense of control and choice.

2. *Optimal health is the product of both physical and mental factors.*

Goals to work for include these:

a) Exercise for at least forty minutes, a minimum of four days a week. Depending on your physical condition, this exercise can be aerobics, weight training, or stretching— but preferably some of each. The yoga exercises can be done as a block or a few at a time, several times daily.

b) Eat consciously. Allow your bodily needs to regulate your diet rather than being a slave to your immediate frame of mind. For most people, unless a physician has prescribed a special diet, guidelines include:

- Low caffeine.
- Low sugar. Sugar releases insulin and increases appetite, leading to further "unconscious eating" (intake not regulated by your body's true needs).

- Low fat. Fat adds excess calories and increases the risk of heart disease and many forms of cancer. Cut down on fatty meat, pastries, cheese, and full-fat dairy products.
- High fiber. Lots of fresh fruits, vegetables, and whole grains increase the movement of food residue through the digestive tract, lower cholesterol levels, and fill you up, the result being reduced appetite and weight loss. They are also a source of vitamins, including the important antioxidant vitamins, A, C, and E, which help the body to neutralize many cancer-causing chemicals.

c) Meditate daily. Practice yields both physiological and psychological benefits. It's important to maintain continuity in any practice, or it gradually fades out. If you don't have ten or twenty minutes for a meditation, take five. Five often stretches to ten and helps you to make progress in the continual deepening of inner peace. Regular practice is the cornerstone on which mini-relaxation-response breaks are built. Since they are conditioned responses, the stronger the association is between breathing and concentration built in long practices, the more effective short meditations and single breaths become.

3. *You could think of yourself as healthy.*

I'm reminded of a former Olympic medalist, skier Jimmy Huega, whose promising career was prematurely terminated by multiple sclerosis (MS). After sinking into a debilitating depression, he realized that he had a choice: He could be a healthy person with MS or an unhealthy person with MS. He began a program of regular physical exercise, proper nutrition, and meditation. His view of himself—when I knew of him during the time I was directing the mind/body clinical programs—was as a superiorly healthy person who also had MS. What's your view of yourself? Is your inner peace completely dependent on your physical condition?

4. *Things change. Change is the only constant in life.*
   If you have commitment—a sense of engagement with life and an openness to purpose and meaning—you receive change with curiosity and openness rather than with fear and doubt. If you feel resistant to change, try letting go and being still for a while. The road has a way of opening in front of you when you don't insist on knowing what the directions are. Remember the wisdom of "don't know"? Allowing yourself to be flexible and receptive, and recognizing that you really don't know what will happen next, allows you to remain open to possibilities. Trying to control the world by insisting that you do know—and can control every aspect of your life—can be a potent prescription for suffering and a limitation on experiencing the "newness" that is the very definition of life.

5. *Your beliefs are incredibly powerful.*
   Consider the following experiment: Women with morning sickness were asked to swallow intragastric balloons as an

objective measure of their stomach contractions and associated nausea. They were then told that they would receive an effective antinausea drug. Instead, they were given syrup of ipecac, a powerful drug used to induce vomiting in cases of poisoning. Most of the women reported reduced nausea and had fewer stomach contractions. The power of their belief was stronger than the drug! Listen to what your mind tells you throughout the day and during your meditations. See what beliefs you hold and how strongly they can influence your perception of the world and of your health. Stay conscious of yourself and choose to believe in a beneficent universe.

6. *The only escape from stress, fear, and doubt is to confront them directly and see them for what they are.*
   Attempts to hide from stress can have only brief apparent effectiveness. In actuality, hiding strengthens the original fear, helplessness, and inability to cope. Attempts to avoid stress through drugs, alcohol, or denial weaken self-esteem. Repression is a mind/body minefield. Becoming unconscious of anything renders you blind and out of control and leads to mental and physical explosions that seem to have no basis since you've chosen not to look. Fears that are faced, even if the act is difficult, lead to a transformation of your attitudes, leaving you with an increased sense of self-worth, control, and inner strength. Sometimes it takes the help of others to confront these "dragons in the cellar." Don't be afraid to ask for help.

7. *Emotions fall into two broad categories: fear and love.*
Perhaps you remember the exercise in which anger, fear, and resentment were experienced in contrast to doing something well, loving or being loved, and experiencing humor. The fear category was associated with the defenses of body-muscle tension, rapid heartbeat, and a sense of holding tight. The love category was associated with openness and a sense of letting go and relaxation. Remember to pay attention to what state your body is in; then check your state of mind. Learning to let go is central to reducing stress and going beyond stress to peace of mind.

8. *Would you rather be right, or would you rather experience peace?*
Ponder during your daily activities and interactions how much energy you use up in defending various positions that make you feel "right," worthy, okay. When you begin to realize your own precious, unique self-worth, the need to defend yourself will diminish, and your body will naturally relax.

9. *Accept yourself as you are* (fat thighs, big noses, mistakes, small bank accounts, health concerns, back pain, or other physical limitations notwithstanding).
This means more than a grudging realization that you'll never again be some way that you used to be or some way that you wish to be. Acceptance means actually honoring yourself as you are now. To the extent that you can honor your inner Self, which, unlike your body or mental capacities, is always whole, you become free. This allows you to

stop judging yourself negatively, which escalates the cycle of anxiety and tension.

10. *Practice forgiveness* (letting go).

See people for who they are instead of who you want them to be. Then accept them as they are rather than judging them for who they're not. The more accepting you become of yourself, the more you can see others in the same light. The core of every human being is the same: unconditioned consciousness, or the Self. See the Self in others. If you are religious or spiritual, you can think in terms of seeing the divine in one another. This is the meaning of the Sanskrit greeting "Namaste."

11. *Stay open to life's teachings.*

There's an old aphorism that when the student is ready, the teacher will appear. The teacher may not come in easily recognizable garb. Sometimes the people who are peskiest or most difficult are the best teachers of patience, assertiveness, forgiveness, or whatever you need to learn. Do you remember the story of the petty tyrant?

12. *Be patient. Patience means mindful awareness.*

The usual understanding of patience is really impatience stretched to the breaking point. Patience is actually mindful attention to life—letting go of the expectations that pull the mind into the past or the future—so that you can remain in the moment without judging or blaming. When you feel impatient, notice it and take a breath of letting go, coming back to the central point of the observer, the Witness that notices without getting carried away by past conditioning. *Practice mindfulness.* Each day remember to do some activity with full attention. This trains your capacity to be mindful in general.

Whether the above attitudes and practices seem close at hand or very far from where you are, they can be realized by anyone who is truly motivated to become free from past conditioning. These goals are not realized in the reading of one book or many. They are a process of gradual unfolding—a gentle awakening rather than a storming of the citadel by force. Like anything of value, self-awareness grows best when nurtured with respect and attention. It's human nature for attention to wander and to seemingly forget things that have been learned. Yet, since all these learnings are stored within the mind, and since new learnings spring from the Self, they can never be completely forgotten. Changes in attitude and understanding may come forward at any time and in ways that surprise and delight you. Be assured that the efforts you have already made will continue to enrich you. Keep your heart and mind on the goal, and go easy with yourself along the way. The goal—to be here now—is closer than you might think.

ADDITIONAL READING

Mind/Body and Stress

Amen, Daniel G., *Change Your Brain, Change Your Life: The Breakthrough Program for Conquering Anxiety, Depression, Obsessiveness, Anger and Impulsiveness*. New York: Three Rivers Press, 1999.

Begley, Sharon, *Train Your Mind, Change Your Brain: How a New Science Reveals Our Extraordinary Potential to Transform Ourselves*. New York: Ballantine Books, 2007.

Borysenko, Joan, *Inner Peace for Busy People: 52 Simple Strategies for Transforming Your Life*. Carlsbad, Calif.: Hay House, 2003.

_____, *Inner Peace for Busy Women*. Carlsbad, Calif.: Hay House, 2004.

Borysenko, Joan, and Gordon Dveirin, *Saying Yes to Change: Essential Wisdom for Your Journey*. Carlsbad, Calif.: Hay House, 2005.

Casarjian, Robin, *Forgiveness: A Bold Choice for a Peaceful Heart*. New York: Bantam, 1992.

Domar, Alice, *Healing Mind, Healthy Woman: Using the Mind-Body Connection to Manage Stress and Take Control of Your Life*. New York: Delta, 1997.

Frankl, Viktor, *Man's Search for Meaning*. Boston: Beacon Press, 2006.

Goleman, Daniel, *Destructive Emotions: A Scientific Dialogue with the Dalai Lama*. New York: Bantam, 2004.

_____, *Emotional Intelligence: Why It Can Matter More Than IQ*, 10th anniversary ed. New York: Bantam, 2006.

Kabat-Zinn, Jon, *Full Catastrophe Living: How to Cope with Stress, Pain, and Illness Using Mindfulness Meditation*. New York: Piatkus Books, 1990.

_____, *Wherever You Go, There You Are: Mindfulness Meditation in Everyday Life*. New York: Hyperion, 2005.

LaRoche, Loretta, *Life Is Short, Wear Your Party Pants*. Carlsbad, Calif.: Hay House, 2003.

Luskin, Fred, *Forgive for Good*. San Francisco: Harper San Francisco, 2003.

Northrup, Christiane, *Women's Bodies, Women's Wisdom: Creating Physical and Emotional Health and Healing*. New York: Bantam, 2006.

Sapolsky, Robert M., *Why Zebras Don't Get Ulcers*. New York: Owl Books, 2004.

Seligman, Martin E.P., *Learned Optimism: How to Change Your Mind and Your Life*. New York: Vintage, 2006.

Sternberg, Esther M., *The Balance Within: The Science Connecting Health and Emotions*. New York: W. H. Freeman, 2001.

Taylor, Shelley, *The Tending Instinct: Women, Men, and the Biology of Relationships*. New York: Owl Books, 2003.

Meditation, Yoga, Spirituality

Benson, Herbert, and Miriam Z. Klipper, *The Relaxation Response*. New York: Harper, 2000.

Borysenko, Joan, *Fire in the Soul: A New Psychology of Spiritual Optimism*. New York: Warner Books, 1994.

_____, *Pocketful of Miracles: Prayers, Meditations, and Affirmations to Nurture Your Spirit Every Day of the Year*. New York: Warner Books, 1994.

Chödrön, Pema, *Comfortable with Uncertainty: 108 Teachings on Cultivating Fearlessness and Compassion*. Boston: Shambala, 2003.

Hanh, Thich Nhat, *Peace Is Every Step: The Path of Mindfulness in Everyday Life*. New York: Bantam, 1992.

_____, *The Miracle of Mindfulness*. Boston: Beacon Press, 1999.

Iyengar, B.K.S., *Light on Yoga*. New York: Schocken, 1995.

Kaplan, Aryeh, *Jewish Meditation: A Practical Guide*. New York: Schocken, 1995.

Keating, Thomas, *Open Mind, Open Heart*. New York: Continuum International, 2006.

Khalsa, Dharma Singh, and Cameron Stauth, *Meditation as Medicine*. New York: Atria, 2002.

McCall, Timothy, *Yoga as Medicine*. New York: Bantam Books, 2007.

Rinpoche, Sogyal, *The Tibetan Book of Living and Dying*. San Francisco: Rider, 2002.

Satchitananda, Swami, *Integral Yoga Hatha*. New York: Holt, Rinehart & Winston, 1975.

Sivananda Yoga Center and Swami Vishnudevananda, *The Sivananda Companion to Yoga*. New York: Fireside, 2000.

Stiles, Mukunda, *Structural Yoga Therapy: Adapting to the Individual*. York Beach, Maine: Weiser Books, 2001.

Vishnudevananda, Swami, *The Complete Illustrated Book of Yoga*. New York: Three Rivers Press, 1995.

Meditation CDs

Borysenko, Joan, *Meditations for Relaxation and Stress Reduction*. Carlsbad, Calif.: Hay House, 2005.

_____, *The Beginner's Guide to Meditation*. Carlsbad, Calif.: Hay House, 2007. Please consult my Web site, www.joanborysenko.com, for many other guided meditation programs.

Kabat-Zinn, Jon, www.mindfulnesstapes.com. You can order mindfulness meditation practice tapes and other audio programs from this site, which also has information on Dr. Kabat-Zinn's lecture and workshop schedule.

Other Resources

Borysenko, Joan, www.joanborysenko.com. Please visit for articles, videos, lectures, descriptions of guided meditation CDs, speaking schedule, and a free newsletter. Ten percent of the profits from book and CD sales go to the Lionheart Foundation's National Emotional Literacy Projects.

The Hoffman Quadrinity Process, www.hoffmaninstitute.org. This excellent eight-day residential program offers participants the possibility of enhanced emotional intelligence, better health, and greater freedom from limiting patterns of thought and behavior. It is offered at several sites in America and abroad. The Hoffman Institute has been operating since 1967, with more than fifty thousand graduates worldwide. Research studies indicate lasting benefits, including decreased anxiety and depression and increased capacity for forgiveness.

LaRoche, Loretta, www.lorettalaroche.com. Happiness, health, and humor based on positive psychology.

Weil, Andrew, www.DrWeil.com. Everything you need to know about healthy living and integrative medicine.

SELF-ASSESSMENT

When I was director of the Mind/Body Clinic, we asked our patients for letters of referral from their physicians so that we could be sure that their medical symptoms had been properly assessed and treated insofar as possible. *For that reason, it is important for you to make sure that any physical symptoms you are experiencing have been properly evaluated before trying any self-help approaches.* Then you can rest assured that no helpful medical treatment has been overlooked.

That said, researchers in the field of wisdom rate self-reflection as the most important kind of wisdom. If you don't know where you are, it's hard to tell which way you're going. For that reason, continuing self-reflection is a cornerstone of minding the body and mending the mind. As you fill out the following questionnaires, you'll likely learn some things about yourself. Should you feel that you need help, based on your awareness of yourself through completing these questionnaires, make sure to seek professional assistance. Clearly, no book or questionnaire can determine your symptoms or provide treatment. At best they are rough guides.

The purpose of this self-assessment is twofold:
- To increase awareness of your physical state and the thoughts, emotions, and behaviors that interact with it.
- To allow you to evaluate yourself *now,* before you begin to learn and apply the tools provided by this book, and *later,* after you feel comfortable using them. For this reason, the self-assessment

forms are printed twice, once as a preevaluation and once as a postevaluation.

The first questionnaire asks about physical symptoms you may experience, their frequency and intensity, and to what degree they interfere with your life. In many cases a physical symptom may not disappear, but it may become less frequent or bothersome.

The second questionnaire asks about thoughts, emotions, and behaviors that can distress people. Your score will reflect how you currently feel, but only you know if those feelings are typical of you and not your reaction to some stressful event that is happening now and may change shortly. It is best to fill out these questionnaires at a time that you feel is "typical" of your life so that they can be used to their best advantage. Wait awhile if you are undergoing an unusually stressful period.

PREEVALUATION
MEDICAL SYMPTOMS CHECKLIST

Please read the following instructions carefully.

What follows is a list of medical symptoms that people sometimes have. Please indicate:

(A) How frequently you have the symptom, *if at all*. Circle a number on a scale of 0 to 7.
(B) The degree of discomfort caused by each symptom you have. Select a number on a scale of 0 to 10.
(C) The degree of interference caused by each symptom you have, that is, how much it interferes with your daily activities. Select a number on a scale of 0 to 10.

For each symptom that you *do have*, be sure to indicate all three responses.

| SYMPTOMS | (A) FREQUENCY | | | | | | | | (B) DEGREE OF DISCOMFORT 0 = None to 10 = Extreme | (C) DEGREE OF INTERFERENCE 0 = None to 10 = Extreme |
	Never or almost never	Less than once a month	Once to twice a month	About once a week	2 to 3 times a week	4 to 6 times a week	Once a day	More than once a day		
1. Headache	0	1	2	3	4	5	6	7	....	....
2. Visual symptoms (e.g., blurred or double vision)	0	1	2	3	4	5	6	7	....	....
3. Dizziness or feeling faint	0	1	2	3	4	5	6	7	....	....
4. Numbness	0	1	2	3	4	5	6	7	....	....

(continues)

SYMPTOMS	Never or almost never	Less than once a month	Once to twice a month	About once a week	2 to 3 times a week	4 to 6 times a week	Once a day	More than once a day	(B) DEGREE OF DISCOMFORT 0 = None to 10 = Extreme	(C) DEGREE OF INTERFERENCE 0 = None to 10 = Extreme
				(A) FREQUENCY						
5. Ringing in the ears	0	1	2	3	4	5	6	7	....	....
6. Nausea	0	1	2	3	4	5	6	7	....	....
7. Vomiting	0	1	2	3	4	5	6	7	....	....
8. Constipation	0	1	2	3	4	5	6	7	....	....
9. Loose stools	0	1	2	3	4	5	6	7	....	....
10. Discomfort with urination (e.g., pressure, burning)	0	1	2	3	4	5	6	7	....	....
11. Abdominal or stomach discomfort (e.g., pressure, burning, cramping) not related to menstruation	0	1	2	3	4	5	6	7	....	....
12. Aching muscles	0	1	2	3	4	5	6	7	....	....
13. Aching joints	0	1	2	3	4	5	6	7	....	....
14. Aching back	0	1	2	3	4	5	6	7	....	....
15. Discomfort in limb(s) (e.g., burning, aching)	0	1	2	3	4	5	6	7	....	....
16. Chest pain (e.g., burning, pressure, tightness)	0	1	2	3	4	5	6	7	....	....

17. Palpitations	0	1	2	3	4	5	6	7
18. Excessive sweating	0	1	2	3	4	5	6	7
19. Shortness of breath	0	1	2	3	4	5	6	7
20. Coughing	0	1	2	3	4	5	6	7
21. Wheezing	0	1	2	3	4	5	6	7
22. Skin problems (e.g., rash, itching)	0	1	2	3	4	5	6	7
23. Teeth grinding	0	1	2	3	4	5	6	7
24. Sleeping difficulties	0	1	2	3	4	5	6	7
25. Fatigue	0	1	2	3	4	5	6	7
26. Other:	0	1	2	3	4	5	6	7
	0	1	2	3	4	5	6	7
	0	1	2	3	4	5	6	7

WOMEN ONLY

1. Vaginal infection or irritation	0	1	2	3	4	5	6	7
2. Menstrual irregularities	0	1	2	3	4	5	6	7
3. Menstrual pain	0	1	2	3	4	5	6	7
4. Premenstrual tension	0	1	2	3	4	5	6	7
5. Premenstrual pain	0	1	2	3	4	5	6	7

PREEVALUATION
PSYCHOLOGICAL SYMPTOMS CHECKLIST
Circle the number, from 0 (never) to 4 (frequently), that represents the degree to
which the following thoughts, feelings, and behaviors have bothered you during
the past month.

THOUGHTS	Never	Rarely	Sometimes	Often	Frequently
1. Awfulizing (taking things to their worst possible outcome)	0	1	2	3	4
2. Blaming myself	0	1	2	3	4
3. Blaming others	0	1	2	3	4
4. Difficulty concentrating	0	1	2	3	4
5. Holding grudges	0	1	2	3	4
6. Thinking and rethinking the same situation	0	1	2	3	4
7. Wishing I could "turn my mind off"	0	1	2	3	4
8. Constantly criticizing other people or situations	0	1	2	3	4
9. Worrying	0	1	2	3	4
10. Thinking something is wrong with my mind	0	1	2	3	4
11. Needing to be right	0	1	2	3	4
12. Feeling out of control	0	1	2	3	4
EMOTIONS					
1. Afraid of specific places or circumstances	0	1	2	3	4
2. Feeling like a victim	0	1	2	3	4
3. Anxious	0	1	2	3	4
4. Blue	0	1	2	3	4
5. Lonely	0	1	2	3	4
6. Irritable	0	1	2	3	4
7. Wanting to throw things or hit people	0	1	2	3	4
8. Guilty	0	1	2	3	4
9. Feeling unfriendly	0	1	2	3	4
10. Uptight	0	1	2	3	4
11. Hopeless about the future	0	1	2	3	4
12. Wanting to "pull the covers over my head"	0	1	2	3	4
13. Feeling that other people don't like me	0	1	2	3	4
14. Upset over criticism	0	1	2	3	4

(continues)

BEHAVIORS	Never	Rarely	Sometimes	Often	Frequently
			BOTHERED		
1. Nail or cuticle biting	0	1	2	3	4
2. Using tobacco in any form	0	1	2	3	4
3. Taking tranquilizers or "street" drugs to change mood	0	1	2	3	4
4. Drinking alcoholic beverages	0	1	2	3	4
5. Chewing gum or sucking candies	0	1	2	3	4
6. Talking a lot	0	1	2	3	4
7. Crying a lot	0	1	2	3	4
8. Sleeping problems (too much or too little)	0	1	2	3	4
9. Eating problems (too much or too little)	0	1	2	3	4
10. Trouble communicating	0	1	2	3	4
11. Avoiding responsibilities	0	1	2	3	4
12. Too much caffeine	0	1	2	3	4

Evaluating the Results

Medical Symptoms Checklist

There is a big difference between having a symptom that interferes with your life and having one that you can live with. In reviewing what symptoms bother you the most, pay close attention to interference. When you take the test again later, compare each symptom that you have reported on all dimensions: frequency, severity, and degree of interference with your life. *When in doubt, always consult a physician.*

Psychological Symptoms Checklist

Everyone experiences some of these symptoms, to various degrees, part of the time. But if you find that many of your responses are in the *often* or *frequently* column (3 or 4), then you are experiencing significant distress and should consider discussing your feelings with a psychotherapist (psychologist, psychiatrist, or social worker specifically trained in psychological counseling). Self-help programs are no substitute for medication when indicated, or individual therapy, but can be very helpful adjuncts to either.

Compare the intensity of your symptoms in the first round with their intensity when you take the test again later. If you feel that your symptoms were bothersome enough that you were hoping for improvement that is not apparent, again you may wish to consider professional help.

Many people are reluctant to seek psychotherapy. They have misconceptions, thinking that only "crazy" people need such help. The truth is that almost every person can profit from psychotherapy. It's a way of learning to be free from past conditioning. Those who choose to go are usually "saner" than the rest of us. All psychologists must themselves receive psychotherapy so that they don't superimpose their own biases on their patients. I can attest to the value of my own therapy—which I continue at least once a month to this day as a form of self-reflection—and hope that you will also keep an open mind toward it.

POSTEVALUATION

MEDICAL SYMPTOMS CHECKLIST

Please read the following instructions carefully.

What follows is a list of medical symptoms that people sometimes have. Please indicate:

(A) How frequently you have the symptom, *if at all*. Circle a number on a scale of 0 to 7.

(B) The degree of discomfort caused by each symptom you have. Select a number on a scale of 0 to 10.

(C) The degree of interference caused by each symptom you have, that is, how much it interferes with your daily activities. Select a number on a scale of 0 to 10.

For each symptom that you *do have*, be sure to indicate all three responses.

SYMPTOMS	(A) FREQUENCY								(B) DEGREE OF DISCOMFORT 0 = None to 10 = Extreme	(C) DEGREE OF INTERFERENCE 0 = None to 10 = Extreme
	Never or almost never	Less than once a month	Once to twice a month	About once a week	2 to 3 times a week	4 to 6 times a week	Once a day	More than once a day		
1. Headache	0	1	2	3	4	5	6	7	....	....
2. Visual symptoms (e.g., blurred or double vision)	0	1	2	3	4	5	6	7	....	....
3. Dizziness or feeling faint	0	1	2	3	4	5	6	7	....	....
4. Numbness	0	1	2	3	4	5	6	7	....	....
5. Ringing in the ears	0	1	2	3	4	5	6	7	....	....

(continues)

SYMPTOMS	(A) FREQUENCY								(B) DEGREE OF DISCOMFORT 0 = None to 10 = Extreme	(C) DEGREE OF INTERFERENCE 0 = None to 10 = Extreme
	Never or almost never	Less than once a month	Once to twice a month	About once a week	2 to 3 times a week	4 to 6 times a week	Once a day	More than once a day		
6. Nausea	0	1	2	3	4	5	6	7	....	....
7. Vomiting	0	1	2	3	4	5	6	7	....	....
8. Constipation	0	1	2	3	4	5	6	7	....	....
9. Loose stools	0	1	2	3	4	5	6	7	....	....
10. Discomfort with urination (e.g., pressure, burning)	0	1	2	3	4	5	6	7	....	....
11. Abdominal or stomach discomfort (e.g., pressure, burning, cramping) not related to menstruation	0	1	2	3	4	5	6	7	....	....
12. Aching muscles	0	1	2	3	4	5	6	7	....	....
13. Aching joints	0	1	2	3	4	5	6	7	....	....
14. Aching back	0	1	2	3	4	5	6	7	....	....
15. Discomfort in limb(s) (e.g., burning, aching)	0	1	2	3	4	5	6	7	....	....
16. Chest pain (e.g., burning, pressure, tightness)	0	1	2	3	4	5	6	7	....	....

17. Palpitations	0	1	2	3	4	5	6	7
18. Excessive sweating	0	1	2	3	4	5	6	7
19. Shortness of breath	0	1	2	3	4	5	6	7
20. Coughing	0	1	2	3	4	5	6	7
21. Wheezing	0	1	2	3	4	5	6	7
22. Skin problems (e.g., rash, itching)	0	1	2	3	4	5	6	7
23. Teeth grinding	0	1	2	3	4	5	6	7
24. Sleeping difficulties	0	1	2	3	4	5	6	7
25. Fatigue	0	1	2	3	4	5	6	7
26. Other:	0	1	2	3	4	5	6	7

WOMEN ONLY

1. Vaginal infection or irritation	0	1	2	3	4	5	6	7
2. Menstrual irregularities	0	1	2	3	4	5	6	7
3. Menstrual pain	0	1	2	3	4	5	6	7
4. Premenstrual tension	0	1	2	3	4	5	6	7
5. Premenstrual pain	0	1	2	3	4	5	6	7

POSTEVALUATION
PSYCHOLOGICAL SYMPTOMS CHECKLIST

Circle the number, from 0 (never) to 4 (frequently), that represents the degree to which the following thoughts, feelings, and behaviors have bothered you during the past month.

THOUGHTS	BOTHERED				
	Never	Rarely	Sometimes	Often	Frequently
1. Awfulizing (taking things to their worst possible outcome)	0	1	2	3	4
2. Blaming myself	0	1	2	3	4
3. Blaming others	0	1	2	3	4
4. Difficulty concentrating	0	1	2	3	4
5. Holding grudges	0	1	2	3	4
6. Thinking and rethinking the same situation	0	1	2	3	4
7. Wishing I could "turn my mind off"	0	1	2	3	4
8. Constantly criticizing other people or situations	0	1	2	3	4
9. Worrying	0	1	2	3	4
10. Thinking something is wrong with my mind	0	1	2	3	4
11. Needing to be right	0	1	2	3	4
12. Feeling out of control	0	1	2	3	4
EMOTIONS					
1. Afraid of specific places or circumstances	0	1	2	3	4
2. Feeling like a victim	0	1	2	3	4
3. Anxious	0	1	2	3	4
4. Blue	0	1	2	3	4
5. Lonely	0	1	2	3	4
6. Irritable	0	1	2	3	4
7. Wanting to throw things or hit people	0	1	2	3	4
8. Guilty	0	1	2	3	4
9. Feeling unfriendly	0	1	2	3	4
10. Uptight	0	1	2	3	4
11. Hopeless about the future	0	1	2	3	4
12. Wanting to "pull the covers over my head"	0	1	2	3	4
13. Feeling that other people don't like me	0	1	2	3	4
14. Upset over criticism	0	1	2	3	4

(*continues*)

BEHAVIORS	BOTHERED				
	Never	Rarely	Sometimes	Often	Frequently
1. Nail or cuticle biting	0	1	2	3	4
2. Using tobacco in any form	0	1	2	3	4
3. Taking tranquilizers or "street" drugs to change mood	0	1	2	3	4
4. Drinking alcoholic beverages	0	1	2	3	4
5. Chewing gum or sucking candies	0	1	2	3	4
6. Talking a lot	0	1	2	3	4
7. Crying a lot	0	1	2	3	4
8. Sleeping problems (too much or too little)	0	1	2	3	4
9. Eating problems (too much or too little)	0	1	2	3	4
10. Trouble communicating	0	1	2	3	4
11. Avoiding responsibilities	0	1	2	3	4
12. Too much caffeine	0	1	2	3	4

INDEX

abdominal breathing, 69–71, 72–75,
  91–92, 224
Abdu'l-Bahá, 103
activities, 64, 102–104, 165–166
acupuncture anesthesia, 11
Ader, Robert, 20
adrenaline, 13
affirmations, 149, 159–160, 169
afflicting thoughts and emotions,
  105–106, 112, 114
AIDS, 206, 215, 216. *See also* Sam's story
aikido student and the drunk, 192
alcohol and nervous system, 57
Alcoholics Anonymous, 195
alcoholism, 143
alexithymia, 174
alienation vs. commitment, 26
allegories
  anxiety cycle, 63–65
  letting go, 124–125, 194–196
  mind/body connection, 213–214
  mindfulness, 100–101, 116–118, 120,
    122
  near-death experiences (NDEs),
    213–215
  out-of-body experience, 213–214
  reframing, 151–152, 153–154,
    161–163
  repressing emotions, 63–65, 171–172
  stress-hardiness, 28–29
  tension, 63–65

See also Sam's story; stories
anger
  breathing consciously and observing,
    120
  as clarifying emotion, 178–179
  effect on mental state, 110, 190
  effect on physiology and health,
    15–16, 184
  guilt as, 189–190
  living in present vs., 109–110
  memory of, 184
  repression of, 64, 171–172
  understanding why someone hurt us,
    191
anxiety
  effect on mental state, 99
  effect on physiology and health,
    15–16, 71
  genie metaphor, 67–68
  in meditation, 58–61
  pain-anxiety-pain cycle, 93
  secondary gains from, 94–95
  source of, 105–106
  from unpredictability, 23, 24–25
  See also worry
anxiety cycle, 63–65, 97–98
anytime series of stretches, 76–82
attention, as anchor for the mind, 43,
  46–47
attitudes
  about pain, 92–95

balanced mental function from, 110
challenges as opportunities, 27
of commitment, 26, 41
emotions and, 178–180
mindfulness and, 102–103
pain tolerance and, 13
practice and, 46
See also reframing
autistic disorders spectrum, 174
autonomic nervous system, 7–8, 66, 71.
     See also breathing
awakening to our true nature, 116, 230
awareness
     of effect from emotions, 184–187
     exercises for cultivating, 104–106
     as first step to a new life, 121–122,
          128, 148
     focus word and, 49
     from honest inquiry without blame,
          136–137
     ignorance is bliss vs., 37–38
     of judgment, 53, 62
     monkey's lack of, 124–125
     of muscle tightness, 51–52
     of nonjudgmental part of the mind, 62,
          115, 122
     as primary goal of meditation, 59
     See also choices
awareness training. *See* meditation
awfulizing experiences, 21–22, 24, 65, 66

back relaxer stretch, 79
back tension, 88
balance
     anytime series for, 76–82, 97–98
     attitudes supporting, 110
     body's natural healing, 6, 7–8
     emotional, 181–183
     in face of attack, 193–194
     mind's limiting habits, 30
Bandler, Richard, 153–154
beginner's mind, 144–145
behavior, as determinant of well-being, 32
behavioral medicine, 95–97, 143,
     174–178
Being of Light in NDEs, 197–199, 210

beliefs, 12–14, 47, 226–227
Bennett-Goleman, Tara, 173
Benson, Herbert, 5, 16–17, 47, 57–58,
     160
Benson–Henry Institute for Mind Body
     Medicine, 5
Beyond the Relaxation Response (Benson),
     47
biofeedback, 65, 74
blame
     honest inquiry without, 136–137
     as mind trap, 139–140, 147–148
     of others or self, 172, 189
     reframing as tool for, 156
blood pressure, tension and, 64–65
body
     awareness of emotions, 186, 187
     brain, 14, 72
     effects of resentment, 189, 200–201
     inability to differentiate reality from
          imagination, 21, 32, 56, 166,
          167–169
     natural healing balance of, 6, 7–8
     response to afflicting thoughts,
          105–106
     response to memories, 60, 96–97
body/mind connection, wisdom of, 94.
     See also mind/body connection
boredom, experience of, 58
Borysenko, Justin
     empathic death experience, 198–199
     hidden agendas of mother and,
          125–127, 140
     owning a car desire, 129–130
     reframing skills of, 157–158
brain, 14, 72
breathing
     abdominal breathing, 69–71, 72–75,
          91–92, 224
     access to changeless place within,
          223–224
     as anchor for the mind, 46–47, 104
     chest breathing, 71–72, 73
     the complete breath, 91–92, 98
     in meditation, 52
     as mindfulness practice, 104

breathing (*continued*)
  overcoming emotional overwhelm, 188
  pain and, 92–97
  pattern changes in, 68–69
  ten-to-one countdown, 75
Buddhism, 37, 95–97, 110, 116, 133, 189

caffeine, 57
cancer, depression and, 15
Casarjian, Robin, 191–192
Castañeda, Carlos, 193–194
cat stretch, 86
cellular responses, from neuropeptides, 14
challenge, 27
change, 23, 25–27, 37–43, 113, 226. *See also* letting go
chest breathing, 71–72, 73
Chidvilasananda, Swami, 189
children
  body's wisdom and, 41
  development of ego, 113–114
  infants, 24, 26, 69
  irritability as call for love, 193
  as mindfulness in action, 102
  needing to be right, 139–140
  reframing technique for, 154–155
choices
  awareness as first step, 121–122, 128, 148
  being right vs., 139–140, 148, 149
  beneficent universe, 227
  conditioning vs., 18, 109–110, 121
  finding meaning in, 26
  for focus word or phrase, 49
  healthy vs. unhealthy, 226
  lifestyle, 2–3
  monkey's lack of, 124–125
  responses as, 53, 55
  "thinking by choice," 112
  See also awareness; letting go
chronic stress, effect on body systems, 28
Cohen, Nicholas, 20
commitment
  as attitude of stress hardiness, 26, 97, 148–149, 186
  change and, 226
  methods for developing, 41–42

as Spirit working through human beings, 222
communities, closeness and health in, 28–29
compassion, focus on, 200
complete breath, the, 91–92, 98
concentration, 44, 48, 102–103. *See also* meditation
conditioned responses
  to closing eyes, 55–56
  helplessness, 25
  of immune system, 20–21
  from mindlessness, 113, 148–149
  reality of original experience, 109
  as unconscious taking over, 18–20, 149–150
conditioning
  choices vs., 18, 109–110, 121
  developing awareness of, 21–22
  letting go of tension as, 57
  needing to be right, 127–128, 139–140
  overview, 106–110
  with shame, 183–184
  to shoulds, 138–139
conditions on happiness, 118, 128
conscious eating, 102, 224–225
conscious mind, 111
control
  as ability to make a positive difference, 26–27
  guilt and false sense of, 32–33
  loss of, 176–178
  from meditation, 41, 59
  paradox of, 35–36
  of reactions to life, 222, 223–224
  as self-doubt, 64–65
  stress as opportunity, 36–37, 45
  See also meditation
coping skills, 25–30
cortisol, 13, 22
craving, 110
creative imagination and visualization, 164–169, 170
creativity, 22–23, 25, 163–164
cyclophosphamide, 20

daily mindfulness exercise, 104
Dalai Lama, His Holiness, the, 31

da Vinci, Leonardo, 217–218
death, 6, 33, 195–196, 203–204
denial, 38–39, 60, 175–176, 185, 227
Denollet, Johan, 175
depression, 15–16, 25, 175
desensitization, 108–109
desires, 117–118, 121, 128–131,
    132–133
despair, 142–143
determination and meditation, 45
diaphragm, 69–70, 71
diaphragmatic breathing, 69–71, 72–75,
    91–92, 224
dirty tricks of the mind, 128–129. See also
    ego; mind traps; suffering
disillusionment, 141–142
distress, heart disease and, 175
Dobson, Terry, 192
Don Juan, 193–194
doubt, confronting directly, 227
dreams, reframing and, 161–163
drug addiction, 143

Easter as metaphor, 36–37
eating consciously, 102, 224–225
eating disorders, 137
effort, meditation and, 45
ego
    desires and, 128–129
    development of, 113–114
    engagement vs., 186
    having vs. being, 113
    interpretation of suffering, 131–133
    overview, 112–113
    as pessimist, 133
    resistance to change, 121–122, 226
    scarcity view of world, 128
    See also mind traps
emotional balance, 181–183
emotional dumping, 177–178
emotional fragility vs. stress-hardiness,
    23–24, 27–30
emotional intelligence, 173–178
Emotional Intelligence (Goleman), 173
emotional mind traps, 173–178
emotional style, 181–187
emotions
    acting out, 176–178

afflicting, 112, 114
of Americans, 2–3
bottling up, 174–176
depression, anxiety, and anger, 15–16
as fear or love, 228
guilt, 30–34, 152, 169–170, 189–190
as healthy mindedness, 178–180
hormones related to, 14
learning from, 187–188
mindless repetition of, 106–107
observing, 183–187, 201
repression of, 24, 171–172
See also anger; fear; feelings; love;
    negative emotions
empathic death experience, 198–199
engagement with life. See commitment
enjoyment, experience of, 43–44
environment as determinant of well-
    being, 32
Erikson, Milton, 164–165
escape, 142–143
even-mindedness, 119, 120
exercise, 224. See also stretching
exhaling the breath, 73

fable, the old man and the genie, 67–68
face exercises, 82
faith
    in ability to change, 145
    author's experience of, 218, 220
    overcoming fear with, 37, 48, 215
    scientific mechanisms of, 12–14
fantasies, 166
fast food epidemic, 2
fat, dietary, 225
fatigue, abdominal breathing vs., 72
fear
    and breathing, 71
    as conditioned response, 109
    confronting directly, 227
    ego's, 114
    emotions as love or, 228
    holding on as, 37
    inner wellspring vs., 116
    living in present vs., 109–110
    mindless repetition of, 106–107
    overcoming phobias, 107–109
feedback, musculoskeletal, 66, 90–91

feelings
  depression, 15–16, 25, 175
  despair, 142–143
  disillusionment, 141–142
  entitlement to, 179
  happiness, 118, 128, 129–131, 138
  unhappiness, 117–118
  See also emotions; helplessness
female/male emotional styles, 182–183
fiber, benefits from, 225
fight-or-flight response, 17–18, 40, 65, 66
final relaxation, 90
flexibility, 83–91, 98
focus word or phrase, 47–48, 49, 52–53
forgiveness, 196–201, 202, 229
forward bend stretch, 87
fountain stretch, 85
full-body relaxer series of stretches,
  83–91, 98
Full Catastrophe Living (Kabat-Zinn),
  95–96
functional magnetic resonance imaging,
  12–13

Gardner, Howard, 172
genetic predispositions, 21, 32
Gibson, George, 1
Goleman, Daniel, 173
gratification of desires, 118–119
gratitude, 169–170, 194, 200–201, 222
gravity as ally, 51–52, 77, 81
Grinder, John, 153–154
guilt, 30–34, 152, 169–170, 189–190

Ham Sah, 49, 53, 208, 224
happiness, 118, 128, 129–131, 138
hardiness. See stress-hardiness
Harvard Heart Letter, 175
headaches, 3–5, 39, 92–95, 171–172
Heading Toward Omega (Ring), 197–198,
  210
healing, curing disease as aspect of, 33
health, public knowledge of, 2
health and well-being, 31–32, 224–226
healthy mindedness, 110–113, 178–180
heart disease, 15, 175, 225
helplessness
  anger as response to, 139–140

from bottling up emotions, 175,
  180–181
control vs., 22–25
human preference for guilt, 33
pain and, 92
pessimist's sense of, 132–133,
  186–187
heredity as determinant of well-being, 32
Hesse, Walter, 16
hidden agendas, 126–127, 148
Hinduism, 116, 133–134
Hoffman Quadrinity Process, 112
Holistic Health and Medicine
  Conference (India), 31
hormones, 13, 14
Huega, Jimmy, 225–226
human nature, 6–7, 178–179, 180, 191,
  222. See also emotions; judgment;
  pain; relaxation response
humor, reframing with, 156–159
hypnosis, reframing with, 160–161
hypothalamus stimulation, 16

identity, 113, 141
ignorance, 110, 144–145
illness, secondary gains from, 94–95
imagination
  body's response to, 21, 32, 56, 166,
    167–169
  fear and, 38
  motion produced by, 165
  scientific mechanisms of, 12–14
  visualization as, 51
immune system, 14–16, 20–21
immunologists, 13–14
indirect hypnosis, 154–155, 161
infants, 24, 26, 69. See also children
inflammation, 15–16
innate responses, 16–18
inner dialogue, 42, 101, 112
inner healing potential, 30, 40–43
inquiry, shift to, 148–149
insomnia, 57–58
inspiration, 164
intellect, 111–112, 182–183
intelligence, multiple forms of, 172–173
intercostal muscles, 70, 72
IQ vs. multiple intelligences, 172–173

James, William, 110
Jampolsky, Gerald, 127, 149, 193
jogging, 45–46
Judge, the, 114, 164. *See also* ego
judgment
  counterproductive nature of, 97
  disengaging from, 116, 119
  ego's role in, 128–129, 131–133
  forgiveness vs., 196–201, 202, 229
  during meditation, 53, 62
  mindfulness vs., 101, 115
  by separate sense of self, 110
  See also ego

Kabat-Zinn, Jon, 95–96, 100, 103–104
Keating, Thomas, 116
Kübler-Ross, Elisabeth, 181
Kutz, Ilan, 5

laughter, benefits from, 170
learned optimism, 187
learned responses. *See* conditioned
  responses
leg extensions stretch, 87
lemon exercise, 165–166
letting go
  allegories about, 124–125, 194–196
  of emotions, 181, 190–191
  enhancing creativity with, 164, 167
  of opinions, 145–146
  of pain, 93–97, 98
  peace of mind from, 120
  of resentments and regrets, 190–191,
    194–196
  of self-importance, 229–230
  surrender, 117–121, 200–201
  of wishing parents were different,
    179–180
  Zen teaching story, 123–124
letting-go stretches, 83
life review in NDEs, 198, 210
lifestyle choices, 2–3
linguistic intelligence, 172
Lionheart Foundation, 191–192
listening to your mind, 115
living in the moment, 8. *See also*
  mindfulness
loneliness, 28

love
  awareness of, 185–186
  emotions as fear or, 228
  experience of, in NDEs, 198–200,
    211–212
  as inner core of human beings, 6–7,
    113–114, 159, 179
  meditation and feeling of, 119–120,
    169
  pain reduction with, 97
  reframing and, 169–170, 191–194
  scarcity mindset vs., 160
  of self, 197, 228–229
  synchronicity related to, 221
Love Is Letting Go of Fear (Jampolsky),
  193
lung function, 15, 69–70

Maddi, Salvatore, 25–27
male/female emotional styles, 182–183
Manhattan (film), 24
mantras, 47–48, 49, 52–53
Maurer, Steve, 110–111, 115, 137,
  158–159
maximizing your experience, 7–8
Mayer, John, 173
McDaniel, Sandra, 20
medical science, 33, 203
medical symptoms, 242
meditation
  affirmations following, 159, 160
  author's introduction to, 4–5
  creative imagination vs., 167–169
  definition of, 60
  effect of, 43, 119–120, 133–135, 225
  experience of, 55–61
  focus word or phrase, 47–48, 49,
    52–53
  meaning of, 43–49
  mindfulness training, 95–97
  physical space for, 61–62
  process for, 50–54, 61–62
  stress-hardiness from, 41
  and the Witness, 115
  yantra for, 217–218
memories, 42–43, 60, 96–97, 184–187
mental conditioning, 106–110. *See also*
  conditioned responses; conditioning

mental health, 28, 39–40, 99, 110, 190
metabolism and meditation, 57–58
migraine headaches, 3–5, 92–94, 95,
    171–172
mind
    distractions perpetrated by, 59–60
    genie metaphor, 67–68
    interpreting body's cues, 66
    memories, 42–43, 60, 96–97,
        184–187
    negative habits of, 53, 65
    ongoing commitment to mending, 148
    as tool, not jailer, 110
    wise utilization of, 32
    worry and, 39–40
    See also observing the mind
Mind/Body Clinic, 5
mind/body connection
    allegory about, 213–214
    author's experience of, 3–5
    breathing pattern changes as, 68–69
    conditioning and, 18–22
    fight-or-flight response as, 17–18, 66
    knowing your limits as, 83
    overview, 13–14
mindfulness
    allegories about, 100–101, 116–118,
        120, 122
    choosing, 119
    exercise for promoting, 104–106
    healthy mindedness, 110–113,
        178–180
    as meditation in action, 101–104
    mental conditioning and, 106–110
    overview, 121–122
    pain relief from, 95–97
    patience as mindful attention to live,
        229–230
    personal integration of, 121–122
    and surrender, 117–121
    See also breathing; meditation;
        stretching
mindfulness meditation, 100, 101
mindlessness, 113, 148–149. See also
    conditioned responses; conditioning
mind traps
    awareness of, 187
    despair, 142–143

disillusionment, 141–142
emotional, 173–178
needing to be right, 127–128,
    139–140, 148, 149, 228
personal put downs, 136–138, 172
rationalization, 140–141
social beliefs, 138–139
See also blame; ego
Miracle of Mindfulness, The (Nhat Hahn),
    103
monkey's lack of choice, 124–125
motivation for meditation, 45
multiple sclerosis, 225–226
multitasking, 64, 102–103
musculoskeletal feedback, 66, 90–91
musical intelligence, 172
mysteries and science, 11–13

names, remembering, 42
naming emotions, 187–188
natural healing balance, 6, 7–8
near-death experiences (NDEs),
    197–200, 210–211, 213–215
neck relaxer stretch, 81
needing to be right, 127–128, 139–140,
    148, 149, 228
negative attitudes, 22–25, 159–160. See
    also mind traps
negative emotions, 15–16, 179–181, 184,
    186
negative encounters, unraveling,
    146–147
negative focus, 53, 65
neurohormones, 13
neurolinguistic programming, 153–154
neuropeptides, 14, 15–16
neuroscientists, 13–14
neurotransmitters, 22
New Age Guilt, 31
Nhat Hanh, Thich, 103
nine-dot puzzle, 152–153
nonafflicting thoughts, 105–106
nonjudgmental awareness, 62, 115, 122
norepinephrine, 22

obesity, 2, 16
observing the mind
    breathing consciously while, 120

for emotional style, 183–187
in interaction with teenagers, 126–127
learning from emotions, 187–188
in meditation, 53–54
nonafflicting and afflicting thoughts,
 105–106
nonjudgmentally, 62, 115, 122
overview, 7–8
pain and, 96–97
suggestions for, 97
as the Witness, 114–117, 118–119,
 128, 194
Oedipus myth, 143
Om, 49
opinions
letting go of, 144–146
as source of suffering, 135–143
opportunities
challenges as, 27
ordinary activities as, 103
people acting hurtfully toward you as,
 191
for reframing, 169–170
staying open to, 29–30, 226, 229
stress as, 36–37, 45
suffering as, 143
optimists, 132–133
Ouelette, Suzanne, 25–27
out-of-body experience, 213–214

Pagels, Elaine, 33
pain
belief in control of source and, 13
breathing and, 92–95
depression and, 15
effect on behavior, 191, 193
from examining hidden agendas, 148
headaches, 3–5, 39, 92–95, 171–172
letting go of, 95–97, 122
as price of denial, 176
See also suffering
pain-anxiety-pain cycle, 93
Passover as metaphor, 36–37
Pasteur, Louis, 163
patience, 229–230. *See also* mindfulness
Pavlov's model, 19, 20
peace of mind
breathing and, 71

even-mindedness as, 119, 120
from fulfillment of desires, 118–119
healing and, 30, 204–206
in meditation, 44–45, 55
in NDEs, 197
physical condition and, 226
See also mindfulness
pelvic tilt stretch, 88
performance anxiety, 59, 65, 76
personal put-downs, 136–138, 172
Pert, Candace, 14
Peseschkian, Nossrat, 103
pessimism, 175
pessimists, 132–133, 186–187
phobia, overcoming, 107–109
physical pain, focusing on, 96–97
physical symptoms vs. underlying causes,
 6
physiology, 15–16, 39–40, 71, 75. *See also*
 mind/body connection; stretching
placebos, subjects' positive reactions to,
 12–13
positive emotions, recording memories of,
 185–187
positron-emission tomography, 12–13
practice, 46, 54
Prigogine, Ilya, 216
progressive desensitization, 108–109
progressive muscle relaxation, 90–91
prospective studies, 15
psyche, breathing as mirror of, 70–71
psychological symptoms, 242
psychologists, 13–14
psychoneuroimmunology, 13–14
psychotherapy, 242
purpose
attitude of commitment and, 26, 27,
 226
for human life, 211, 214, 219, 222

Ram Dass, 121
rationalization, 140–141
reactions, personal control of, 223–224
reality, resistance to, 118, 152. *See also*
 reframing
reasoning, 111–112, 172–173, 182–183
rebirth, Easter and Passover as symbols
 of, 36–37

reframing
with affirmations, 159–160
allegories about, 151–152, 153–154,
161–163
attack as need for love, 191–193
attacker as teacher, 193–194
with creative imagination and
visualization, 164–169
creativity and, 163–164
with dreams, 161–163
with humor, 156–159
with hypnosis, 160–161
looking for opportunities, 169–170
nine-dot puzzle, 152–153
of pain, 93
technique for children, 154–155
as tool for staying stuck, 156
regressive coping, 27–28
regrets, 189–194, 201–202
relationships
analyzing other people, 147–148
emotional style and, 182–183
and mind traps, 135–143
taking responsibility for your part in,
145–146, 148
relaxation, 55, 59, 90–91. See also
breathing; peace of mind; stretching
relaxation response
breathing and, 71, 75
with creative imagination, 166–167
from induction phase of hypnosis, 160
meditation as access to, 41, 44–45
overview, 16–17, 40
processes leading to, 29–30
as substitute for sleep, 58
relaxed state for overcoming phobia,
107–109
REM sleep, 56
repression, results of
allegory about, 63–65
inability to understand yourself, 227
type C personality, 174–175
uncovering with meditation, 60–61
research methods, 13–14, 15, 28
resentment, 189–194, 201–202
resistance
to change, 121, 122, 226
to pain, 93, 96–97

to reality, 118, 152
utilizing energy tied up in, 155
responsibility
acceptance of, 145–146, 148
analysis of "New Age Guilt," 31–32
assuming fault vs., 137
meditation and, 41
optimist's healthy view of, 133
for your process, 148
Ring, Kenneth, 197–198, 210
role models, utilizing, 149
Roseto, Penna., 28–29
Roshi, Suzuki, 145

Sales, St. Francis de, 54, 58–59
Salovey, Peter, 173
Sam's story
"Amazing Grace" serendipity, 219, 220,
221
author's inspiration from, 221–222
as he lay dying, 217–218, 220–221
mutual connection with author,
208–212
out-of-body experience allegory,
213–214
overview, 8, 204–205
peace of mind consult request, 204,
206–207
theory of "dissipative structures" and,
216
science of healing
brain, mind, and molecules, 13–14
conditioned responses, 18–22
faith, belief, imagination, and, 11–13
and guilt, 30–34
and hardiness, 25–30
and helplessness, 22–25
innate responses, 16–18
negative emotions, 15–16
secondary gains, 94–95
sedentary lifestyle, 2, 16
Self, the, 115, 118–119, 179, 228–229
self-absorption, cost of, 2–3, 229–230
self-assessment, 8–9, 235–236, 242
self-assessment questionnaires, 237–241,
243–247
self-care, 50, 62, 178–180
self-deprecation, 136–138, 142–143

self-love, 197, 228–229
self-observation, 97–98, 235–236, 242.
    See also observing the mind
self-understanding, 172, 179
Seligman, Martin, 2, 24–25, 132–133,
    186–187
separation, 26, 128–129, 139–140,
    147–148, 200. *See also* ego
Shakespeare, William, 36
shoulder shrugs, 80
shoulds, 138–139, 172
Siegel, Bernie, 214
Sifneos, Peter, 174
sigh of relief, 74–75
sleep, restful vs. stressful, 56–57
Smith, G. Richard, 20
smoking, and immune system, 16
social experiences, reconnecting with,
    28–29
social intelligence, 172–173
society, 138–139, 176. *See also*
    conditioned responses; conditioning
spirituality
    of awareness, 49
    form of, 214, 215
    of inspiration, 164
    power of beliefs, 47, 226–227
    and similarities in humanity, 116
    See also faith
stories
    faith, 218, 220
    genie metaphor, 67–68
    meditation, 4–5
    migraine headaches, 3–5, 92–94, 95
    Oedipus myth, 143
    Zen teaching stories, 123–124, 144
    See also allegories; Borysenko, Justin
stress
    acute vs. chronic, 22–25
    confronting directly, 227
    as current lifestyle choice, 2
    fight-or-flight response and, 17–18
    headaches from, 3–5, 39, 92–95,
        171–172
    inability to control, 22–23
    as opportunity, 36–37, 45
    source of, 14
    See also tension

stress-hardiness
    allegory about, 28–29
    emotional fragility vs., 23–24, 27–30
    for facing change, 37, 41–43
    three C's of, 25–27
    truth in principles of, 222
    See also commitment; control
stretching
    anytime series, 76–82, 97–98
    full-body relaxer series, 83–91, 98
    for relaxing the body, 76
success, 173, 200
suffering
    Americans' attitude toward, 37
    attempting to avoid, 38
    denial and, 38–39, 60, 175–176
    desires and, 129–131
    essence of, 118, 124
    from imaginary disasters, 131, 132–133
    inevitability of, 130–131
    as motivation to examine ourselves, 143
    from opinions, 135–143
    from unawareness, 148
    understanding vs., 144–145
    See also pain
sugar, effect of, 224
surrender, 117–121, 200–201. *See also*
    letting go
synchronicities, 214, 221

Temoshok, Lydia, 174
tension
    allegory about, 63–65
    anytime series vs., 76–82, 97–98
    chest breathing and, 71–72
    from denial and fear, 38–39, 227
    from fight-or-flight response, 17–18,
        40, 65, 66
    letting go of, 77–78
    from musculoskeletal feedback, 66
    pain and, 92–93
    secondary gains from, 94–95
    See also stress
ten-to-one countdown, 75
thinking
    inner dialogue, 42, 101, 112
    physical results of, 14, 165–166
    role in health, 32

thinking by choice, 112
thoughts
    awfulizing with, 21–22, 24, 65, 66
    emotional awareness and, 186–187
    nonafflicting and afflicting, 105–106,
        112, 114
three C's of stress-hardy personalities,
    25–27
time perception, 210
transcendental meditation, 16
transformational coping, 27, 33
12 brief reminders, 223–230
type C personality, 174–175
type D behavior, 175

unconditioned mind, 118. See also
    Witness, the
unconscious mind, 18–20, 57, 111,
    159–163. See also conditioned
    responses; conditioning
understanding, 144–149
unfinished business, 194–196
unhappiness from desires, 117–118
unhealed emotional child, 112
unpredictability, 23, 25, 33

Vaillant, George, 28
victim mentality. See helplessness

victim vs. observer, 146
visceral feedback from awfulizing
    thoughts, 66
visualization
    of breath, as loving attention, 96–97
    of breathing process, 51, 73–74, 91–92
    creative imagination and, 164–169

Wallace, R. Keith, 16–17
wall hang stretch, 83
Weiss, Jay, 23
Wherever You Go, There You Are (Kabat-
    Zinn), 100
wholeness, 33–34
Wilbur, Ken, 31
wisdom, understanding leading to,
    146–147
Witness, the, 114–117, 118–119, 128,
    194. See also observing the mind
worry, 39–40, 41, 53, 131, 132–133. See
    also anxiety; tension

yantra, 217–218
yoga and meditation as minivacation, 4
yoga classes, 98
Yoga Sutras of Patanjali, 133–134

Zen teaching stories, 123–124, 144